Con
Mı
Guide

There are 47 individual Wildlife Trusts covering the whole of the UK and the Isle of Man and Alderney. Together The Wildlife Trusts are the largest UK voluntary organization dedicated to protecting wildlife and wild places everywhere – at land and sea. They are supported by 800,000 members, 150,000 of whom belong to their junior branch, Wildlife Watch. Every year The Wildlife Trusts work with thousands of schools, and their nature reserves and visitor centres receive millions of visitors.

The Wildlife Trusts work in partnership with hundreds of landowners and businesses in the UK. Building on their existing network of 2,250 nature reserves, The Wildlife Trusts' recovery plan for the UK's wildlife and fragmented habitats, known as A Living Landscape, is being achieved through restoring, recreating and reconnecting large areas of wildlife habitat.

The Wildlife Trusts also have a vision for the UK's seas and sea life – Living Seas, in which wildlife thrives from the depths of the oceans to the coastal shallows. In Living Seas, wildlife and habitats are recovering, the natural environment is adapting well to a changing climate, and people are inspired by marine wildlife and value the sea for the many ways in which it supports our quality of life. As well as protecting wildlife, these projects help to safeguard the ecosystems we depend on for services like clean air and water.

All 47 Wildlife Trusts are members of the Royal Society of Wildlife Trusts (Registered charity number 207238). To find your local Wildlife Trust visit wildlifetrusts.org

Concise Mushroom Guide

NEW HOLLAND

First published in 2011 by New Holland Publishers (UK) Ltd
London · Cape Town · Sydney · Auckland
www.newhollandpublishers.com
Garfield House, 86–88 Edgware Road, London W2 2EA, UK
80 McKenzie Street, Cape Town 8001, South Africa
Unit 1, 66 Gibbes Street, Chatswood, New South Wales 2067, Australia
218 Lake Road, Northcote, Auckland, New Zealand

10 9 8 7 6 5 4 3 2

ISBN 978 1 84773 785 4

Series Editor: Krystyna Mayer
Design: Alan Marshall
Production: Melanie Dowland
Publisher: Simon Papps

Additional thanks to Ray Tantram for reading the text on behalf of The Wildlife Trusts.

Reproduction by Modern Age Co. Ltd., Hong Kong
Printed and bound in China by Leo Paper Group

Other titles in series

Concise Bird Guide
Concise Butterfly & Moth Guide
Concise Wild Flower Guide
Concise Garden Wildlife Guide
Concise Tree Guide
Concise Seashore Wildlife Guide

Contents

Introduction

Several thousand species of fungi occur in Europe, including Britain and Ireland. Many are microscopic, and although they are important to agriculturists due to the damage they can cause to crops, they are not considered in this book.

The species included in this book are mainly those that can be readily recognized because they have some distinguishing character in terms of appearance, smell or taste. They are arranged in family groups. Diameter measurements are given for caps and fruit bodies, height measurements for stems. Although some fungi are described as associating with specific trees, there are exceptions when the host tree may be of a different species from that stated. However, relatively few species grow on both deciduous and coniferous trees.

A far greater number of fungi fruit in the autumn than in the spring. Most may be found in May to October in northern areas, and a month later in southern areas; in most years the peak months are August to September and September to October respectively. In a mild winter some species continue fruiting right through into spring.

What Are Fungi?

Fungi lack the pigment chlorophyll, which is contained in green plants, so are unable to make use of the sun's energy to build up the carbohydrates from which a plant is formed. Instead, like animals, they get their energy through the breakdown of organic matter. In addition, the hard parts of fungi are chemically closer to the chitin that forms the casing of insects, than to lignin, which forms the hard parts of plants. These extraordinary organisms are grouped in the fungi kingdom, which is separate from plants, animals and bacteria.

A mushroom or toadstool is only the fruit body or reproductive part of an extensive network of very fine threads that branch, join and weave below the surface of the ground, breaking down decaying material for sustenance. In the same way, the bracket fungus that grows on a tree is the fruit of a body of fine threads that penetrate the substance of the wood. This network is known as the ***mycelium*** and is common to all fungi. The individual threads, or ***hyphae***, are invisible to the naked eye, but often a number cluster together to form visible threads about the thickness of sewing cotton. Certain fungi form even thicker black threads like bootlaces, known as ***rhizomorphs***, which may be seen under the loose bark of dead trees.

The mycelium is perennial and certainly persists in the soil for decades, probably for centuries and possibly for millennia. It plays a major part in the rotting down of autumnal leaves, which would quickly be metres deep without this process of decomposition.

Not all fungi limit themselves to the breakdown of leaves, however. Many send their hyphae down to the roots of trees and form a network in the outer layers of the finer roots. Here a mutual interchange of material, known as mycorrhizal symbiosis, occurs to the benefit of both fungus and tree, and without which the tree would not prosper. It is believed that the fungal hyphae are able to take up and transfer to the tree minerals such as phosphates, and to receive from the tree compounds that they are unable to synthesize, such as sugars. Foresters regard the fungal element in the soil as very important.

Identifying Fungi

Nature has explored every avenue of shape, texture and colour in fungal fruit bodies, ranging from cups to finger-like projections, caps on stalks to irregular potato-like lumps buried in the ground, soft jellies to brackets too hard to be cut with a knife, and brilliant red to turquoise. However, the typical mushroom fruit body consists of a ***cap*** and ***stem***.

Cap

The cap is generally round. Beneath it are the spore-bearing surfaces, which may be either flat vertical plates known as ***gills***, or ***tubes*** that end in openings known as ***pores***. Gills may run down the stem (***decurrent***), be free of the stem (***free***), or be attached to it along their entire length (***adnate***) or by a short decurrent tooth or notch (***sinuate***), depending on the genus.

Stem

The stem is usually attached to the centre of the cap, but may also be attached at the edge. It may have a firm or fragile ***ring***. This is formed from a membrane (the ***partial veil***) that protects the developing gills of the young mushroom and breaks away from the edge of the cap as it opens. The stem base may be contained in a bag known as the ***volva***, which is the remains of the sheath (the ***universal veil***) that completely surrounds both cap and stem as the fruit body grows, rupturing as the mushroom rises from the ground. Both veils may or may not be present. It is essential to recognize them if the fungus is to be identified correctly. The volva is a characteristic of some of the most deadly poisonous fungi – the Amanitas.

Tree Associations

It is helpful to note which trees are in the vicinity of fungi that are being identified, because some are quite specific in their associations. It is also useful to ascertain if a fungus is growing on the ground or on wood, which may not be very obvious if the wood is buried.

Fungi Divisions

All fungi have the same basic structure of hyphae and reproduce by means of spores, but the way in which they arrange their spores separates them into two main phyla: Basidiomycota and Ascomycota.

Basidiomycetes allow their spores to fall into the passing air currents, so they have to elevate their fruit bodies at least a short way above the ground. The spores are formed on the stalks of cells known as ***basidia***, and there are usually four to a cell. The Basidiomycota includes boletes, mushrooms, chanterelles, bracket fungi, stinkhorns, earthstars, puffballs, jelly fungi, smuts, bunts and rusts.

Ascomycetes form their spores in tubes like gun barrels, known as ***asci***, which usually point upwards. When ripe, the spores are forcibly ejected for several millimetres, which is enough to get them airborne. In some species small changes in humidity or air pressure are enough to initiate this release and, as many asci discharge at the same time, the spores appear as a little puff of smoke. The largest phylum of fungi, the Ascomycota includes morels, cup fungi, truffles, brewer's yeast and baker's yeast.

Perhaps fortunately, very few fungal spores ever germinate, or at least few develop into further organisms. For this reason they are released in enormous numbers, an average mushroom producing 10 to 20 thousand million. The Giant Puffball (page 168) has been calculated to produce more than seven billion spores from a single fruit body of average size.

Conservation of Fungi

There has been a marked decline in a number of fungi in continental Europe through collecting for eating, pollution, loss of habitat and trampling. In Britain there has been little commercial collecting, and no recent declines are attributable to it. However, reduction in numbers of British species that has been noted has been due to destruction of habitat through the use of inorganic fertilizers on pasture land, conversion of heathland and deciduous woodland to conifer plantations, and the removal of dead wood for fuel.

POISONOUS FUNGI

Edible fungi are not generally identified in this book, because this is a field guide rather than a guide to the edibility of fungi. It is essential that anyone collecting mushrooms is able to identify *absolutely* those species that are edible. If there is *any* doubt about a particular specimen, an expert opinion should be sought. Serious cases of poisoning – up to death – have occurred through the failure to recognize all the distinguishing features of a species, and through confusion between similar-looking poisonous and non-poisonous species.

Yellow-cracked Bolete

Boletus subtomentosus

Size and description Cap to 10cm; stem to 8cm. Similar to *B. cisalpinus* (opposite). Cap mid- to cigar-brown, covered initially with yellowish velvety down that wears off, allowing yellow cracks to appear. Pores dirty lemon-yellow, blueing slightly on bruising. Flesh creamy to yellow, not changing when damaged. Stem mainly brown with a brick-red base, but creamy in upper part.

Habitat Common in mixed deciduous woodland, occurring in small groups. Widespread in Europe.

Season Summer to late autumn.

Bolete species

Boletus cisalpinus

Size and description Cap to 11cm; stem to 8cm. Cap shades of hazel-brown, initially with a slightly velvety texture that soon wears off, leaving it smooth and cracking. Pores dirty yellow, bruising blue or green. Flesh medium thickness, cream or straw, with a thin reddish layer immediately under the cuticle; it often turns pink where it is damaged by slugs. Stem usually flushed red along the entire length except for the very top, which is yellowish.

Habitat Common in deciduous woodland, particularly with oaks.

Season Midsummer to late autumn.

Summer Bolete

Boletus reticulatus

Size and description Cap to 12cm; stem to 15cm. Cap cinnamon-brown; bun shaped, with a suede-like texture that becomes dry and tends to crack. Pores very small, round, and white tending to olive-green. Flesh white and firm. Stem swollen and bulbous, pale brown and completely covered with a white network or reticulation.

Habitat Grows singly or in small groups under deciduous and coniferous trees, but particularly associated with oaks and beeches. Uncommon but widespread in Europe.

Season Early summer to autumn.

Cep

Boletus edulis

Size and description Cap to 25cm; stem to 15cm. Large and thick fleshed. Cap brown, typically with a pale margin; rounded when young, then flattened. Pores white, becoming creamy-grey, then yellow. Flesh white and pleasant smelling. Stem pale grey with a white net, particularly at the top. One of the best edible species.

Habitat Found in woodland of all types, particularly with beeches and oaks, growing in small groups. Widespread in Europe, although rarer in north and declining.

Season Early summer to autumn.

Bay Bolete

Boletus badius

Size and description Cap to 14cm; stem to 10cm. Cap shades of dark brown, smooth and shiny. Pores large, angular and lemon-yellow, bruising bluish-green. Flesh pale yellowish turning pale blue-green where cut. Stem stout and paler than cap.

Habitat Grows in small groups, most frequently with conifers, but also with beeches. Common in Europe, with an uneven distribution.

Season Midsummer to autumn.

Old Man of the Woods

Strobilomyces strobilaceus

Size and description Cap to 15cm; stem to 12cm. Cap convex, and covered and overhung with thick ragged scales that are initially white, then black interspersed with grey. Flesh soft and white, turning red, then dark brown when cut. Stem concolorous with cap, scaly and paler above rough sheathing ring.

Habitat Grows in small scattered groups on soil in deciduous woodland, and occasionally coniferous woodland. Unevenly distributed in Europe and rare in Britain.

Season Late summer to autumn.

Slippery Jack

Suillus luteus

Size and description Cap to 10cm; stem to 10cm. Cap chestnut-brown paling to sepia at the edge, covered with slippery gluten in wet weather. Pores and tubes dirty yellowish and small. Flesh pale, almost white, greying in the stem base. Stem whitish at the base, yellower nearer the top, with a large and floppy ring that is initially pale but darkens almost to the cap colour.

Habitat Occurs in small groups in coniferous woodland, particularly with Scots Pine. Common and widespread in Europe.

Season Midsummer to autumn.

Shallow-pored Bolete

Suillus bovinus

Size and description Cap to 10cm; stem to 6cm. Cap pale cinnamon-brown with a persistently paler margin, and covered with slippery gluten. Pores pale grey to cinnamon-brown; large, irregular and slightly decurrent. Flesh slightly yellowish, becoming clay-pink on exposure; darker in the stem. Stem parallel, similar in colour to the cap and usually somewhat short.

Habitat Grows in small groups under two-needled pines, particularly Scots Pine. Widespread throughout Europe.

Season Midsummer to autumn.

Grey Larch Bolete

Suillus viscidus

Size and description Cap to 10cm; stem to 9cm. Cap pale buff with olive-grey blotches; convex, with a slimy surface layer. Pores large, angular and grey, bruising greenish. Flesh thick, soft and whitish, turning faintly blue where cut. Stem cylindrical, pale straw above the ring and greyish below.

Habitat Grows solely in association with larches, occurring in small groups. Rare in Britain but more common in continental Europe.

Season Early summer to autumn.

Larch Bolete

Suillus grevillei

Size and description Cap to 10cm; stem to 11cm. Cap golden-yellow to rusty-orange; convex, with a slimy surface layer. Pores small and angular, lemon-yellow bruising reddish-brown. Flesh thick, soft and pale yellow. Stem brownish-yellow below a slimy membranous white ring, yellow above it.

Habitat Grows only in association with larches, occurring in small groups. Common and widespread in Europe, including Britain.

Season Midsummer to autumn.

Brown Birch Bolete

Leccinum scabrum

Size and description Cap to 15cm; stem to 10cm. Usually large, but varies greatly in size. Cap snuff-brown and rounded; it feels as though it is filled with cotton wool. Pores off-white. Flesh white, unchanging when cut. Stem tall and white, covered with blackish scales.
Habitat Occurs in birch woods in scattered groups, often in large numbers. Widespread in Europe with an uneven distribution.
Season Late summer to autumn.

Orange Birch Bolete

Leccinum versipelle

Size and description Cap to 20cm; stem to 20cm. Frequently large bolete. Cap orange, dry and much firmer to the touch than that of Brown Birch Bolete (opposite). Cap cuticle often forms an overhanging skirt. Pores small and greyish. Flesh white, rapidly darkening to blue-green when cut, and soon becoming nearly black in both the stem and cap. Stem white covered with brownish-black scales, bruising black.

Habitat Associated with birches, growing in scattered groups. Widespread and unevenly distributed in Europe.

Season Summer to autumn.

Granulated Bolete

Suillus granulatus

Size and description Cap to 9cm; stem to 8cm. Cap yellowish to reddish-brown; convex, then flattened as it expands; contains a sticky surface layer that is easily removed. Pores small, round and pale lemon-yellow, releasing droplets of milky fluid that darkens on drying. Flesh thick and pale yellow. Stem cylindrical, solid, and cream or pale yellow, with white or yellowish granules developing near the apex.
Habitat Grows in small groups on sandy soil under or near coniferous trees. Common and widespread in Europe.
Season Late summer to autumn.

Chestnut Bolete

Gyroporus castaneus

Size and description Cap to 10cm; stem to 8cm. Cap cinnamon- to chestnut-brown; convex and smooth. Pores small, round and white, becoming lemon-yellow and bruising brownish. Flesh thick and white. Stem smooth, brittle and almost hollow.

Habitat Grows in small groups on acidic sandy soils in deciduous woodland, particularly with oaks. Unevenly distributed in Europe, favouring warm areas. Rare in Britain.

Season Midsummer to early winter.

Bitter Bolete

Tylopilus felleus

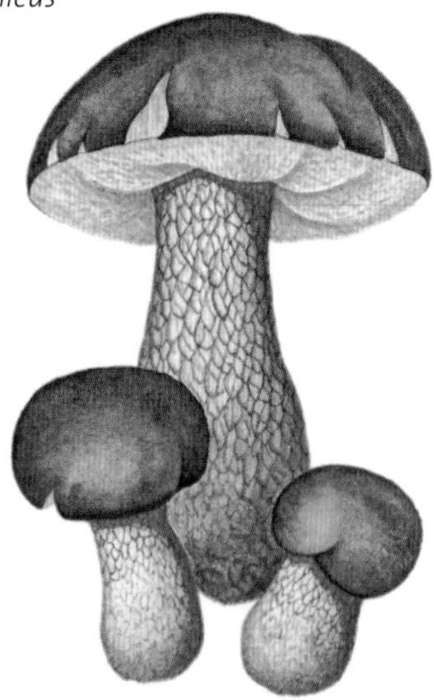

Size and description Cap to 12cm; stem to 10cm. Cap snuff-brown; rounded at first, but often becoming inverted so that the pinkish tubes are visible. Flesh white or cream, later becoming pinky-buff. Stem thick, pale at first but darkening to approach the cap colour and covered in a brown net.

Habitat Found mainly in deciduous woodland, particularly with beeches and oaks. Often occurs on acid soils. Widespread but occurs infrequently.

Season Summer to autumn.

Curry Milkcap

Lactarius camphoratus

Size and description Cap to 5cm; stem to 5cm. Cap reddish-brown; convex at first, becoming flattened to slightly funnel shaped, and sometimes with a small umbo (raised bump) at maturity. Flesh thin and pale rusty-brown; it releases a watery white latex when cut. Gills pale reddish-brown, crowded and running on to the stem, which is cylindrical and concolorous with the cap.

Habitat Grows under conifers, particularly spruces, in widely scattered groups. Widespread and quite common in Europe.

Season Midsummer to autumn.

Coconut Milkcap

Lactarius glyciosmus

Size and description Cap to 5cm; stem to 7cm. Cap greyish-lilac; convex at first and later flattened. Gills pinkish-buff; crowded and running on to the stem. Flesh firm and white with a strong scent of coconut oil; exudes a white latex when cut. Stem brittle, concolorous with the cap and bruising brown.

Habitat Grows in damp soil under birches, occurring in scattered groups. Widespread and quite common in Europe.

Season Late summer to autumn.

Saffron Milkcap

Lactarius deliciosus

Size and description Cap to 15cm; stem to 6cm. Cap reddish-orange; convex at first, but becoming funnel shaped with an incurved margin. Gills orange-yellow bruising green; crowded and and running on to the stem. Flesh thick, firm and brittle, creamy yellow and exuding a bright yellow latex when cut. Stem short and stout, concolorous with the cap, and often developing salmon-pink blotches in shallow pits.

Habitat Occurs in scattered groups under conifers, particularly pines and spruces. Common and widespread in Europe; most frequent in north.

Season Late summer to autumn.

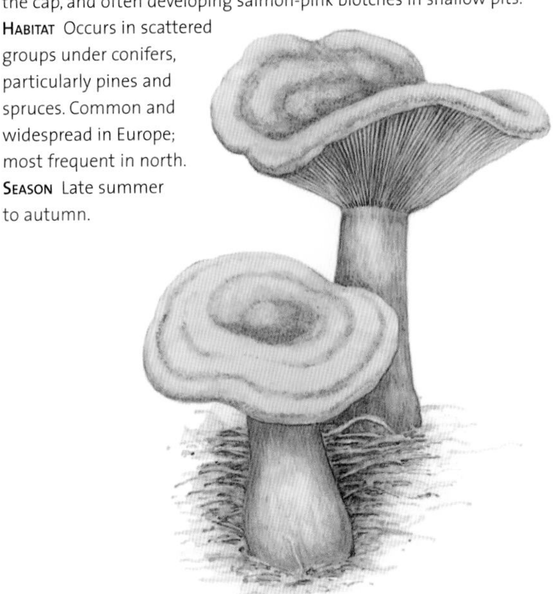

Woolly Milkcap

Lactarius torminosus

Size and description Cap to 10cm; stem to 7cm. Cap salmon-pink with indistinct darker concentric bands, and covered with long tangled hairs like matted wool. Gills cream with a pinkish flush; slightly decurrent. Flesh fairly thick; milk white. Stem short to medium, sturdy, pale flesh in colour and hairless.

Habitat Grows in damp soil under birches. Widespread and common.

Season Late summer to autumn.

Sweet Milkcap

Lactarius subdulcis

Size and description Cap to 7cm; stem to 6cm. Cap cinnamon-brow; convex at first, then becoming flattish with a small umbo. Gills pinkish; crowded and running on to the stem. Flesh thin and white, releasing a copious white latex with an oily odour. Stem cylindrical and concolorous with the cap.

Habitat Occurs in scattered groups under deciduous trees. Common and widespread throughout Europe.

Season Midsummer to early winter.

Slimy Milkcap

Lactarius blennius

Cap to 9.5cm; stem to 7cm. Cap various shades of brown and greenish-grey, often with blotches of darker colour in concentric zones; rounded at first, later funnel shaped; slimy. Gills white, becoming grey; slightly decurrent. Flesh whitish; milk white, drying grey. Stem short and sturdy, and greyish-cream. Grows under deciduous trees, generally beeches. Widespread and common. Occurs late summer to autumn.

Rufous Milkcap

Lactarius rufus

Cap to 10cm; stem to 8cm. Cap reddish-brown to rusty; dry and almost always with a central umbo. Gills white tinged with the cap colour; slightly decurrent. Flesh and milk white. Stem paler than the cap. Grows with pines, especially in wet places. Common and widespread. Occurs summer to late autumn.

Ugly Milkcap

Lactarius turpis

Cap to 15cm; stem to 7cm. Cap dark olive-brown to dark grey; thick and with a central depression when old. Gills creamy; decurrent. Flesh white, browning when cut; milk white. Stem concolorous with the cap or paler, stout and short. Grows under birches, often in grass or leaf litter. Common and widespread. Occurs late summer to autumn.

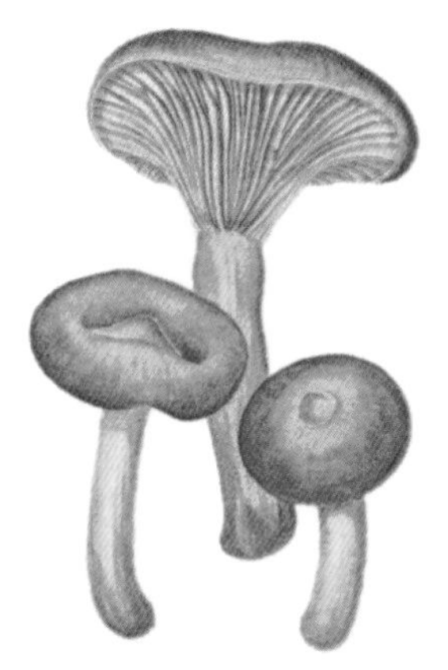

Birch Milkcap

Lactarius tabidus

Cap to 5cm; stem to 6cm. Cap orange-buff, usually with a central umbo. Gills yellower than cap; decurrent. Flesh whitish and rather thin; milk white turning yellow on a white cloth. Stem tall, similar in colour to the cap. Grows in deciduous woodland, especially with birches. Widespread and common. Occurs midsummer to autumn.

Oak Milkcap

Lactarius quietus

Size and description Cap to 8cm; stem to 7cm. Cap dull reddish-brown with indistinct concentric darker and lighter zones and a central umbo. Gills paler than the cap; slightly decurrent. Flesh pale buff, thickish in the cap and often hollow in the stem; milk whitish. Stem long and cylindrical, sometimes with a tapered base, similar in colour to the cap, but darkening towards the base. Smell oily, said to be reminiscent of bed bugs.

Habitat Grows only in the vicinity of oak trees. Widespread and extremely common.

Season Autumn.

Charcoal Burner

Russula cyanoxantha

Size and description Cap to 15cm; stem to 10cm. Cap may be almost any colour, but is typically dull lilac. Gills white; sometimes forked, and crowded; distinguished by a greasy flexible feel when a finger is rubbed over them. Flesh white and of medium thickness. Stem average in thickness, white, hard and occasionally with a flush of the cap colour.

Habitat Grows in scattered groups in deciduous woodland. Widely distributed and common throughout Europe.

Blackening Russula

Russula nigricans

Size and description Cap to 20cm; stem to 7cm. Large, thick and extremely brittle russula. Cap, gills and stem all-white to cream. Gills well spaced and adnate; intermediate gills present. Flesh hard and white, initially changing to red, then blackish-brown; when cut it turns first greyish-pink, then dark grey. Eventually the whole fungus turns blackish-brown, but it is slow to decompose so entirely dark ones are most commonly found. Stem short, stout and cylindrical, similar in colour to the cap.

Habitat Grows in all kinds of woodland, but commonly occurs with beeches. Widespread and common.

Season Midsummer to early winter.

Common Yellow Russula

Russula ochroleuca

Cap to 10cm; stem to 7cm. Cap ochre-yellow; exact shade of yellow makes it recognizable in the field once it has been encountered a few times. Gills pale cream; adnate. Flesh white and of medium thickness. Stem white, greying with age. Grows with a wide variety of trees, both deciduous and coniferous, and is one of the most common russulas throughout the season. Occurs late summer to early winter.

Yellow Swamp Russula

Russula claroflava

Cap to 10cm; stem to 6cm. Cap distinctive bright yellow. Gills pale ochre; almost free of the stem. Flesh white and of medium thickness. Stem medium to tall, and white. Gills and other parts bruise grey. Pleasant smell. Grows under birches in wet boggy places. Widespread and common. Occurs summer to autumn.

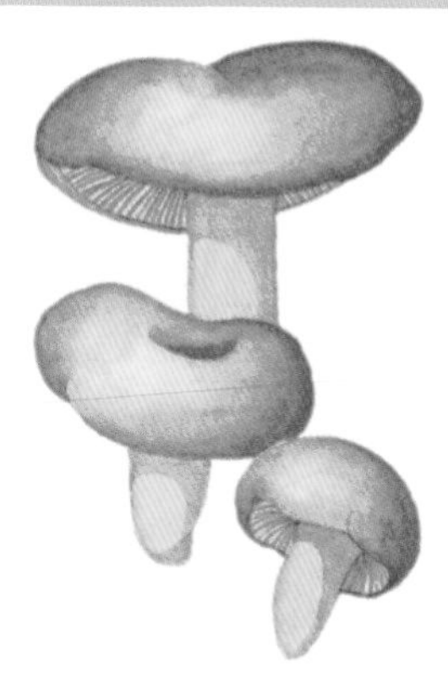

Geranium Russula

Russula fellea

Cap to 9cm; stem to 7cm. Cap honey-ochre. Gills paler than cap; adnate. Flesh almost white. Stem a paler shade of the cap colour, and stout and firm. The distinguishing feature of this fungus is its marked aroma of geranium leaves. Grows under beeches. Widespread and common. Occurs autumn.

Crab Russula

Russula xerampelina

Cap to 15cm; stem to 7cm. Cap ranges in colour from brown to purple, yellow or even green. Gills pale to medium ochre; adnate, fairly thick and deep, and connected by ridges where they join the cap. Flesh white and moderately thick. Stem stout, white and sometimes tinted pink. Distinguished by smelling of crab, particularly when old. Found mainly under beeches and oaks. Widespread and common. Occurs late summer to early winter.

Bare-toothed Russula

Russula vesca

Cap to 10cm; stem to 10cm. Cap thickish, of various colours, usually pale wine to buff. Cuticle tends to shrink from the margin, leaving the gill edges exposed. Gills white; adnate and closely packed, some showing forking close to the stem. Flesh white. Stem stout, white and sometimes tinted pink. Common among deciduous trees, often beeches and oaks. Occurs mid-summer to early autumn.

Primrose Russula

Russula sardonia

Cap to 10cm; stem to 8cm. Cap reddish to purple, sometimes brownish. Gills primrose to golden-yellow; adnate or slightly decurrent. Flesh thick. Stem stout and cylindrical, and white usually overlaid with a strong purplish flush. Smell often of stewed apples. Common in coniferous woodland. Occurs summer to autumn.

Beechwood Sickener

Russula nobilis

Size and description Cap to 7cm; stem to 5cm. Cap shades of bright red; first hemispherical, then convex and finally flat with a shallow depressed centre. Gills white; adnate. Flesh white and with a faint smell of coconut. Stem medium to tall, tapering only slightly upwards, and white, tinged ochre. Poisonous in quantity, causing sickness.
Habitat Grows under beeches. Widespread and common.
Season Autumn.

Purple Russula

Russula atropurpurea

Size and description Cap to 10cm; stem to 6cm. Cap shiny and dark, almost black in centre, and reddish or purple around the sides; initially hemispherical, later convex or flat with a depressed centre. Gills pale cream; adnate and closely spaced. Flesh and stem white. Smells pleasantly of apples.

Habitat Grows in deciduous woodland with oaks and beeches; occasionally found under conifers. Widespread and very common.

Season Summer to autumn.

Stinking Russula

Russula foetens

Size and description Cap to 20cm; stem to 12cm. Cap brownish-ochre and slimy, with a furrowed margin; hemispherical at first, becoming flatter with a depressed centre. Gills dirty cream; thick, spaced and adnate. Flesh white with cavities in the stem, which is short, stout and whitish. Distinguished by its strong rancid smell.

Habitat Grows in old deciduous woodland, usually with oaks and beeches. Common.

Season Summer to autumn.

Panthercap

Amanita pantherina

Cap to 10cm; stem to 10cm. Cap pale brown; convex, then flattened, and covered with white patches of volval remains. Gills, flesh and stem white. Stem does not turn pink when damaged (as does that of the similar-looking edible Blusher, page 47, with which it can be confused). Poisonous and can be fatal. Found in the same habitat as Blusher, but much rarer. Grows in deciduous woodland, usually with oaks and beeches. Occurs summer to autumn.

False Deathcap

Amanita citrina

Cap to 10cm; stem to 8cm. Cap lemon-yellow with large white patches; initially hemispherical, then flat. Gills white; almost free. Flesh white. Stem with a ring, and swollen into a large bulb at the base. All parts have a strong aroma like that of raw potatoes, especially when cut. Also found as a white form (*alba*). Easily confused with the lethally poisonous Destroying Angel (page 44). Grows in many types of woodland, often in association with beeches. Occurs midsummer to autumn.

Deathcap

Amanita phalloides

Size and description Cap to 12cm; stem to 15cm. Cap whitish with central radiating fibres of green or sometimes yellow; hemispherical, then convex to flat. Gills white (differentiating it from edible mushrooms); free. Flesh white. Stem white, usually with a ring, but often the veil that forms the ring remains hanging on the cap edge instead; stem base surrounded by a marked sac-like volva. Lethally poisonous: causes liver and kidney failure, and eating just half a cap can cause death. Accounts for about 96 per cent of fungus fatalities.
Habitat Occurs in woodland, usually under oaks.
Season Summer to autumn.

Fly Agaric

Amanita muscaria

Size and description Cap to 20cm; stem to 23cm. Most readily recognized of all toadstools. Cap brilliant red, usually with white spots that may be lost and the colour washed out of the cap, leaving it orange; hemispherical, then convex and finally flat. Gills white; free. Stem cylindrical and white with a ring. Poisonous: not as deadly as Deathcap (opposite) and Destroying Angel (page 44), and has hallucinogenic properties.

Habitat Grows mostly with birches. Widespread and very common in suitable locations.

Season Late summer to early winter.

Destroying Angel

Amanita virosa

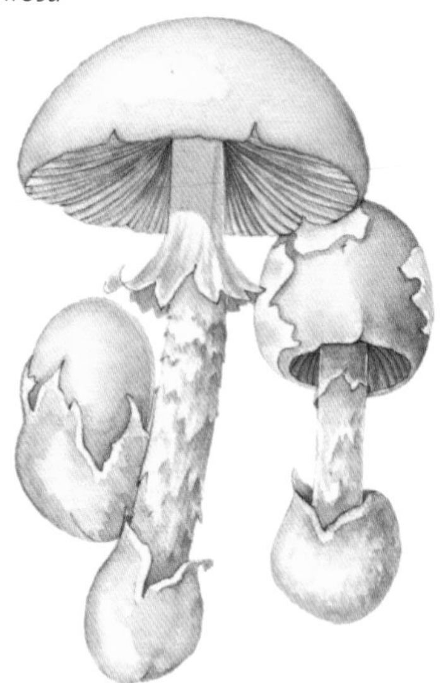

Size and description Cap to 10cm; stem to 12cm. Cap all-white; conical at first, turning flatter with a lopsided appearance. Gills white; free. Stem white, scaly or shaggy with a volva and ring. Sickly sweet smell. Deadly poisonous: effects like those of Deathcap (page 42).

Habitat Grows in deciduous or mixed woodland, often among oaks and birches. Less common in south than Deathcap, but more common in north and west; in Britain most common in Scotland, where it is widespread.

Season Late summer to autumn.

Tawny Grisette

Amanita fulva

Size and description Cap to 10cm; stem to 12cm. Cap tawny with marked striations radially placed all around the outer margin; initially ovoid, then convex and finally flat with a depressed centre and broad umbo. Gills and flesh white. Stem white and without a ring, and with a large and conspicuous volva flushed with the cap colour.

Habitat Grows in open deciduous woodland, particularly with birches. Widely distributed and common in Europe.

Season Late summer to autumn.

Caesar's Mushroom

Amanita caesarea

Size and description Cap to 18cm; stem to 15cm. Cap bright orange-red, turning yellow with age; smooth and shiny with fine lines at the margin, and hemispherical when young, expanding to convex with age. Gills yellow; crowded and free. Flesh whitish with a pleasant odour. Stem yellow with a pendulous, often striped ring; bulbous base encased in a large white volval sac from which the stem breaks cleanly.

Habitat Grows in deciduous woodland, particularly oakwoods. Appearance sporadic in southern Europe.

Season Late summer to autumn.

Blusher

Amanita rubescens

Size and description Cap to 15cm; stem to 15cm. Sturdy medium to large fungus. Cap reddish-brown covered with grey patches; hemispherical at first, becoming convex then flattened with age. Gills white; free. Flesh white. Stem white, turning pink, especially where damaged by slugs, broadening towards the base; it has a ring which, on its outer surface, shows striation formed from contact with the gills. Reddening of the flesh of this fungus, especially in the stem base, is diagnostic.

Habitat Found singly or in scattered groups in mixed deciduous woodland, where birches are present. Widespread and extremely common in Europe.

Season Midsummer to autumn.

Parrot Waxcap

Hygrocybe psittacina

Size and description Cap to 4cm; stem to 7cm. Cap and stem basically cream to yellow, but both typically covered with a slippery green gluten that persists patchily all over. Stem top remains green when the rest of the green colour has disappeared. Gills white, although they often look greenish because of the gluten collected between them; adnate. Flesh whitish.

Habitat Grows on grassland in poor pasture and open woodland. Widespread and common.

Season Midsummer to late autumn.

Blackening Waxcap

Hygrocybe conica

Size and description Cap to 10cm; stem to 10cm. Smallish waxy toadstool. Conical cap, which opens with maturity, may start by being yellow, orange or even red, but very soon starts to turn black unevenly. Gills, which are well hidden at first, are whitish. Flesh yellowish-white. Stem tall and cylindrical, coloured as the cap. Eventually the whole fungus becomes completely black, without initially losing its shape. Also called Witch's Hat.

Habitat Grows in grassland. Widespread and common across northern Europe.

Season Midsummer to autumn.

Crimson Waxcap
Hygrocybe punicea

Cap to 15cm; stem to 25cm. Cap bright blood-red at first, but colour soon washes out with rain or frost, leaving the surface looking as though it is covered with a white bloom; cap rounded-conical in shape. Gills pale yellow and reddish at the base; adnate. Stem red with a white base; if split with a knife the flesh of this fungus is white. Grows only in good-quality unimproved grassland. Occurs autumn.

Golden Waxcap
Hygrocybe chlorophana

Cap to 7cm; stem to 8cm. Small and predominantly yellow. Gills and flesh a consistent lemon-yellow, which is the diagnostic feature. Stem tall, smooth, slimy and often channelled; same colour as the cap or slightly paler. Grows in grassland, and found in open woodland, fields, lawns and roadsides. Occurs spring to autumn.

Scarlet Waxcap

Hygrocybe coccinea

Size and description Cap to 6cm; stem to 6cm. Cap blood-red; bell shaped at first, later becoming more convex or flat. Gills initially yellow but becoming blood-red with age; fairly widely spaced. Flesh orange-red, and fibrous with no distinctive odour. Stem hollow and blood-red, sometimes paler at the base.

Habitat Grows on pastures and lawns, and in grassy open woodland. Widespread across Europe.

Season Late summer to early winter.

Herald of Winter

Hygrophorus hypothejus

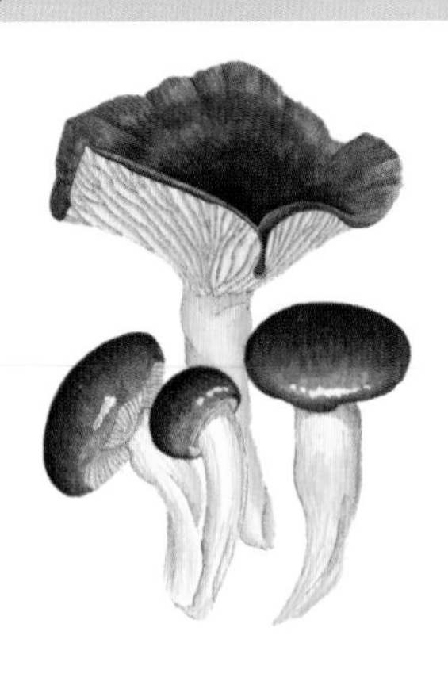

Cap to 6cm; stem to 8cm. Cap dull olive-brown, covered with olivaceous gluten, slightly more pallid at the margin; convex at first, becoming flatter and with a sharp umbo. Gills yellowish and slippery with gluten, especially below the ring zone; decurrent. Stem pallid yellow, sometimes tinged with orange. Grows in needle litter, usually in pine woods. Occurs late autumn to early winter.

Gold-flecked Woodwax

Hygrophorus chrysodon

Cap to 15cm; stem to 7cm. Small and fairly stout agaric. Cap white, yellowing with age, with an incurved margin and yellow granules. Gills white; adnate. Flesh white, soft and thick. Stem proportionally stout, basically white, but covered with fine yellow granules. Grows singly or in scattered groups in deciduous woodland, mainly under beeches. Occurs late autumn to early winter.

Honey Fungus

Armillaria mellea

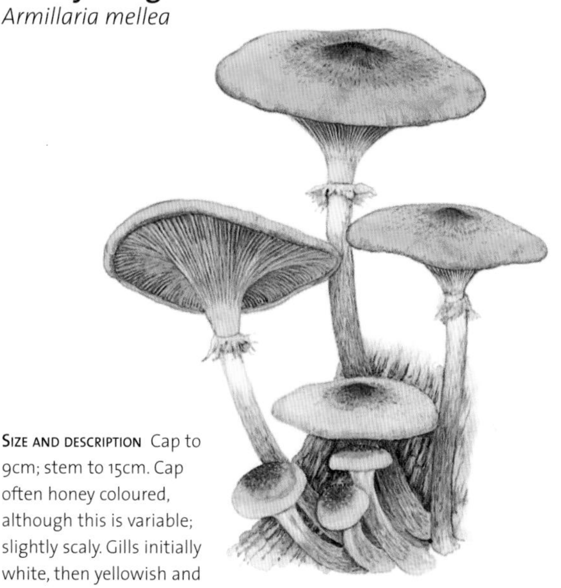

Size and description Cap to 9cm; stem to 15cm. Cap often honey coloured, although this is variable; slightly scaly. Gills initially white, then yellowish and finally brown; slightly decurrent. Flesh white. Stem similarly coloured to the cap and bears a white ring. Grows in tufts; lower caps often coloured with white spores shed by higher caps. Parasitic and responsible for the deaths of many trees and shrubs in woodland and gardens. Also called Bootlace Fungus because it spreads by means of bootlace-like black cords.

Habitat Grows in dense clusters on deciduous and coniferous trees, which it often destroys. Widespread and common in England; most frequent in Scotland.

Birch Knight

Tricholoma fulvum

Size and description Cap to 10cm; stem to 11cm. Cap tawny, usually with slightly darker streaks radiating around the edge; first convex, then flatter and usually with a low umbo. Gills yellow spotting brown with age; adnate. Flesh yellow. Stem slim and cylindrical, concolorous with the cap but paler at the top. Both the cap and stem are sticky when moist.
Habitat Grows singly or in groups on wet acidic soils in woodland, and is usually associated with birches. Widespread and extremely common.
Season Autumn.

Grey Knight
Tricholoma terreum

Size and description Cap to 7cm; stem to 8cm. Cap grey with a fibrous felty surface that may split as the cap expands; bell shaped at first, becoming umbonate. Gills greyish-white; fairly widely spaced. Flesh white to pale grey. Stem long and cylindrical, white and silky smooth.

Habitat Occurs in large groups on calcareous soils in coniferous and occasionally deciduous woodland. Fairly common throughout Europe, but has an uneven distribution.

Season Late summer to autumn.

Aniseed Agaric

Clitocybe odora

Size and description Cap to 7cm; stem to 6cm. Cap a mixture of greens and blues; convex when young, later becoming whitish and flat with an incurved margin. Gills paler than the cap; crowded and running down the stem. Flesh whitish and tough with a strong odour of aniseed. Stem base slightly swollen and covered in fibrous white down.

Habitat Grows in small troops in leaf litter in deciduous woodland or grassy clearings. Quite common in Europe.

Season Autumn to early winter.

Fragrant Funnel

Clitocybe fragrans

Size and description Cap to 4cm; stem to 6cm. Cap yellowish-brown when wet, drying to cream with a darker centre, and finely lined at the margin; cap flattish, often becoming depressed in the centre with age. Gills whitish-buff; crowded and running down the stem. Flesh thin and white with a strong odour of aniseed. Stem concolorous with the cap.
Habitat Grows in tufts or small troops in moss or grass in deciduous woodland. Widespread in Europe but uncommon.
Season Autumn to early winter.

Clouded Funnel

Clitocybe nebularis

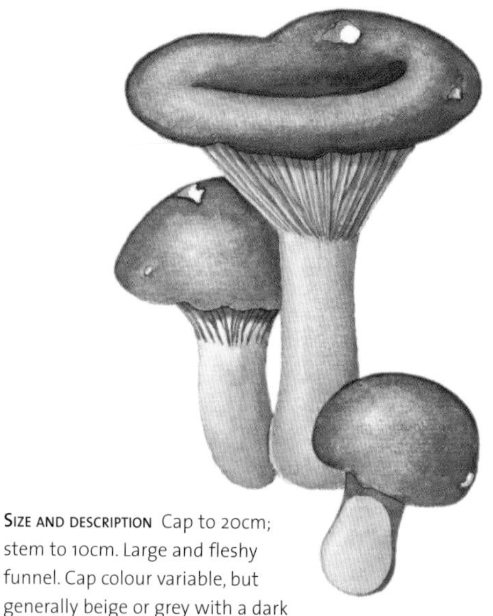

Size and description Cap to 20cm; stem to 10cm. Large and fleshy funnel. Cap colour variable, but generally beige or grey with a dark centre; convex, becoming flatter and usually slightly depressed in the centre. Gills creamy or greyish; decurrent. Flesh whitish. Stem sturdy, widening towards the base and similar in colour to the cap. Strong sweet smell.

Habitat Grows in clusters, mainly in deciduous woodland. Widespread and common.

Season Autumn to early winter.

Trooping Funnel
Clitocybe geotropa

Size and description Cap to 20cm; stem to 15cm. Cap convex and yellowish-buff when young, becoming shallowly funnel shaped and flesh coloured with age. Gills concolorous with the cap; crowded and running down on to the stem. Flesh thick, white and firm with a mealy odour. Stem stout and cylindrical.

Habitat Occurs in rings or troops in grassy clearings in mixed or deciduous woodland, particularly on calcareous soils. Widespread in Europe but nowhere common. In Britain most common in south.

Season Autumn.

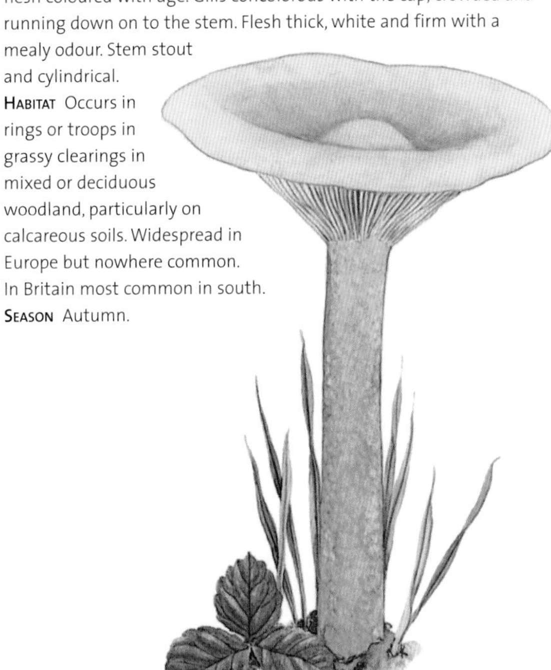

Common Funnel

Clitocybe gibba

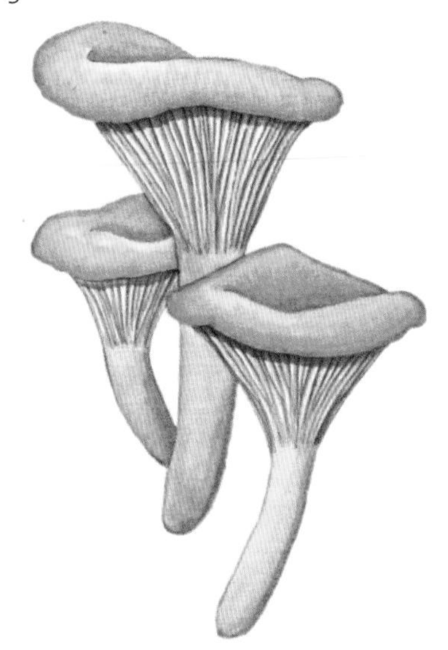

Size and description Cap to 8cm; stem to 8cm. Cap a pale washed leather colour; funnel shaped even when young, smooth and silky, becoming more expanded with an undulating margin. Gills creamy-white with a pink tinge. Stem short and slim, often with a slightly swollen base; concolorous with the cap or paler. Distinct sweetish or almond odour.

Habitat Grows in scattered groups in leaf litter in deciduous woodland and on heaths. Widespread and common.

Season Summer to autumn.

Ivory Funnel
Clitocybe dealbata

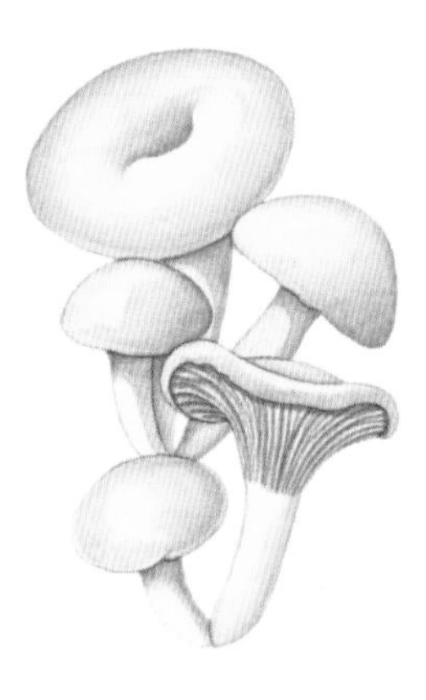

Cap to 4cm; stem to 4cm. Cap white or ivory; flattish convex, expanding almost to funnel shape. Gills adnate or slightly decurrent. Flesh and stem white. Whitewashed or chalky appearance. Grows in groups or rings and is rather slimmer than a mushroom. Poisonous: extremely toxic and has caused death by being mistaken for a mushroom and eaten. Grows in groups on lawns and in short grassland, often with Fairy Ring Champignon (page 71). Widespread and common. Occurs midsummer to late autumn.

Club Foot
Ampulloclitocybe clavipes

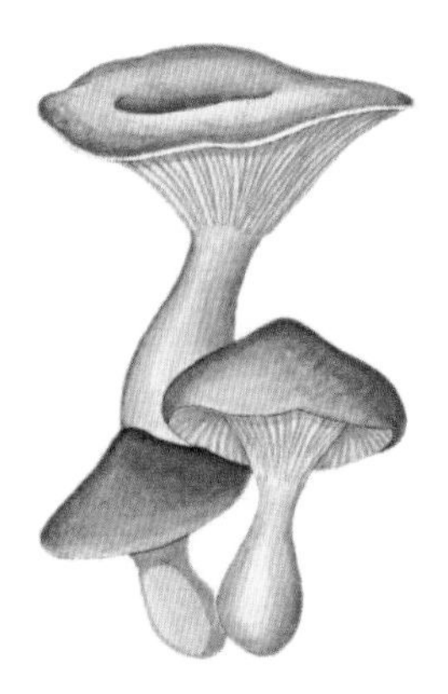

Cap to 8cm; stem to 7cm. Cap grey-brown; rounded or flat, retaining an incurved edge; surface smooth and velvety. Gills creamy-white; decurrent. Flesh white. Club-shaped stem, swollen towards the base. Grows mainly with beeches and birches, in leaf litter. Widespread and common. Occurs autumn.

Amethyst Deceiver

Laccaria amethystina

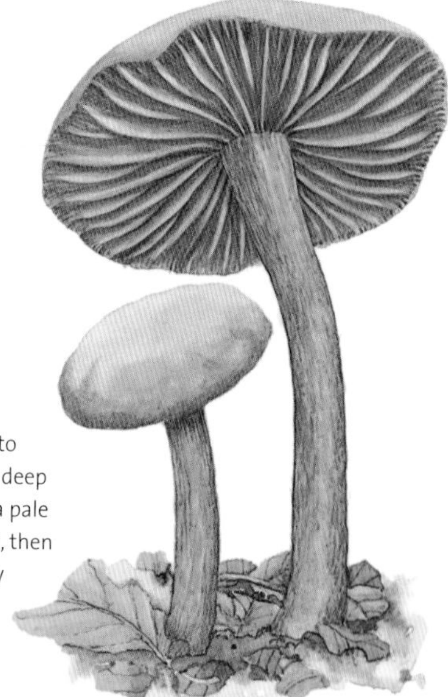

Size and description Cap to 5cm; stem to 10cm. Cap deep purplish-lilac drying to a pale lilac-buff; convex at first, then flattened and eventually concave with a wavy margin. Gills the same colour as the cap, becoming white and powdery with spores; widely spaced. Flesh concolorous, tough and fibrous. Stem concolorous with the cap, and covered with whitish fibres towards the apex and lilac fibres near the base.

Habitat Grows singly or in scattered groups in deciduous and coniferous woodland, particularly with chestnuts and beeches. Common and widespread across Europe.

Season Midsummer to early winter.

The Deceiver

Laccaria laccata

Size and description Cap to 5cm; stem to 10cm. Very variable in appearance and habitat, hence its common name. Cap brick-red although extreme variability of colour and shape often cause it to be misidentified. Gills concolorous with the cap, or with a rosy-pinkish tinge, becoming powdered white with spores; well spaced and adnate. Stem tall in relation to size of the cap; fibrous and twisted.
Habitat Grows in scattered groups in almost any situation, from deciduous and coniferous woods to cultivated lawns. Very common across Europe.
Season Midsummer to early winter.

Russet Toughshank

Collybia dryophila

Cap to 5cm; stem to 6cm. Small and very variable fungus that is responsible for much of the leaf decomposition in deciduous woodland. Cap thin and variable in colour, but usually pale. Gills white; free. Flesh white and thin. Stem thin and hollow, widening and darkening towards the base. Grows in all types of deciduous woodland, and under bracken on heaths. Widespread and common. Occurs midsummer to late autumn.

Wood Woolly-foot

Collybia peronata

Cap to 6cm; stem to 6cm. Cap pale grey to brown. Gills yellow with age; free. Flesh creamy. Stem fairly long, depending on the depth of the leaf litter in which it grows; pale, yellowing with age; base covered with hair. Grows singly or in groups in deciduous woods, and may occur with conifers. Widespread and common. Occurs late summer to autumn.

Spotted Toughshank

Collybia maculata

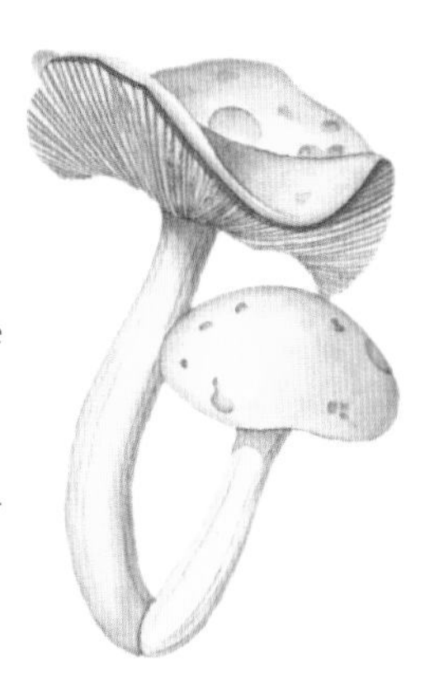

Cap to 10cm; stem to 10cm. Cap white or cream; convex, then flatter with an incurved margin that becomes wavy with age. Gills free. Stem colour as cap, and may be elongated according to the depth of the medium in which it grows. All parts, particularly the cap and gills, develop brownish spots with age. Grows in leaf litter of deciduous or coniferous woods, or in bracken litter. Widespread and common. Occurs midsummer to late autumn.

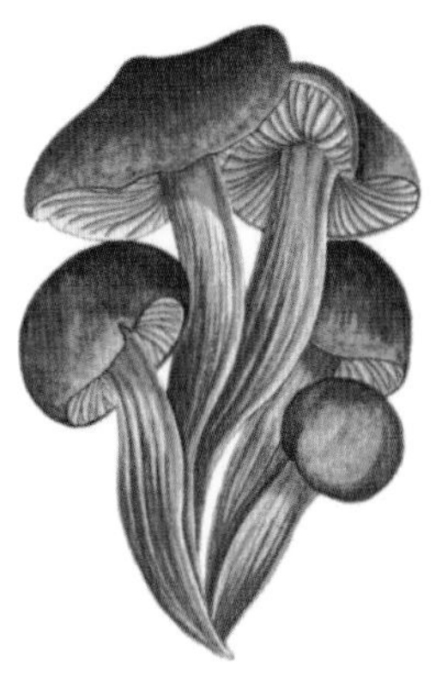

Spindleshank

Collybia fusipes

Cap to 7cm; stem to 9cm. Cap brown and smooth. Coarse, broad gills fawn coloured and free. Flesh fawn. Stem flushed with cap colour, longitudinally grooved, widening and darkening towards the centre and tapering towards the base, which forms quite a long 'root'. Densely clustered growth method makes the fungus easy to identify. Grows on oaks and is generally found close to the bases of trees. Widespread and common. Occurs spring to early winter.

Lilac Bonnet

Mycena pura

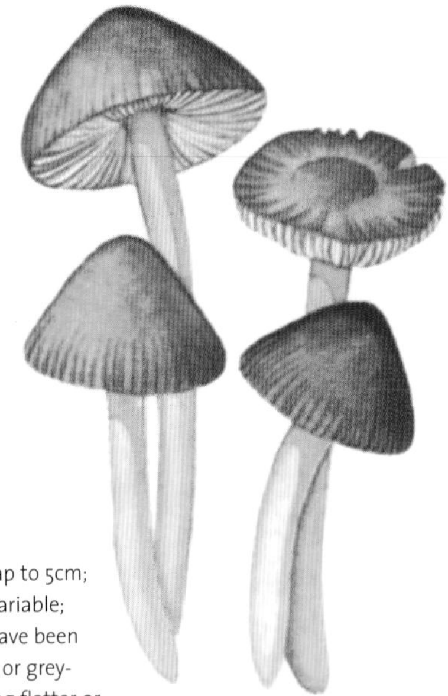

Size and description Cap to 5cm; stem to 6.5cm. Very variable; numerous varieties have been described. Cap pinky- or grey-brown; convex, turning flatter or bell shaped, and usually umbonate. Gills white with a lilac tint; adnate. Flesh white. Stem white, rather stouter and shorter than the stems of other species in the genus. Can be recognized by its smell, which is reminiscent of radishes. Poisonous: can cause hallucinations.

Habitat Usually grows singly or in small groups in deciduous leaf litter. Widespread and common.

Season Summer to early winter.

Common Bonnet

Mycena galericulata

Size and description Cap to 6cm; stem to 10cm. Cap grey, drying brownish; conical, expanding to bell shaped with a shallow umbo. Gills white, although developing a flesh-pink tint with age; adnate. Flesh white. Stem long, similar in colour to the cap, smooth, shiny and tough.

Habitat Grows in tufts or sometimes singly on decayed or buried deciduous wood, particularly oak logs and stumps. Very common and widely distributed in Europe.

Season Late spring to early winter.

Milky Bonnet

Mycena galopus

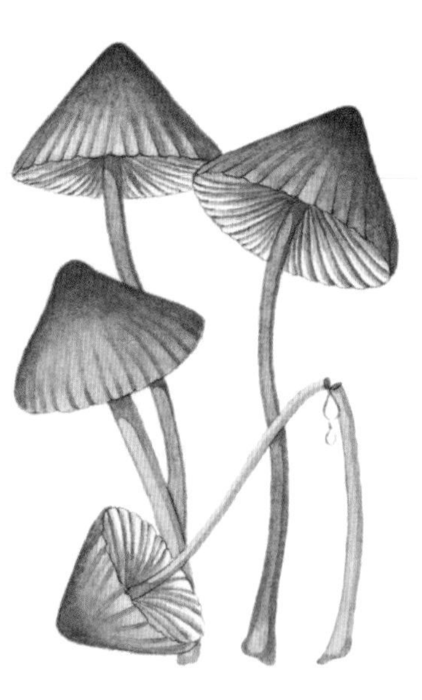

Size and description Cap to 2cm; stem to 8cm. Very variable. Cap pale umber-grey, darker in the centre; conical, bell shaped or flatter. Gills flesh-white; adnate. Stem long and thin, grey, with a white cottony base; oozes white milk when cut or broken, hence its common name.

Habitat Grows in tufts in deciduous leaf litter and among grasses in mixed woodland and hedgerows. Widespread and extremely common.

Season Late summer to late autumn.

Burgundydrop Bonnet

Mycena haematopus

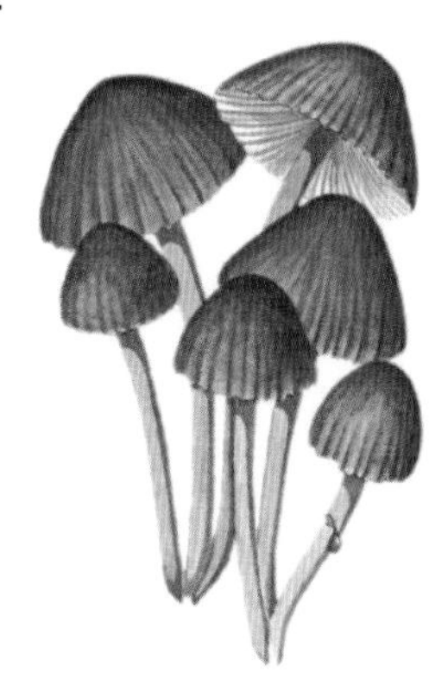

Cap to 4cm; stem to 7cm. Small and tufted species. Cap greyish-brown drying much paler, but often showing streaks or blotches of a darker colour; conical, then bell shaped or flatter. Gills flesh-white when undamaged; adnate. Stem similar in colour to the cap; when cut it oozes drops of blood-red sap. Grows on dead deciduous wood and stumps. Occurs late summer to autumn.

Yellowleg Bonnet

Mycena epipterygia

Cap to 2cm; stem to 5cm. Variable bonnet. Cap pale grey or yellowish. Gills dirty white; adnate. Flesh concolorous with the gills. Stem tall in relation to the size of the cap, and pale grey covered with a layer of yellowish gluten, especially at the stem top; when picked up it will adhere to the fingers. Grows in leaf litter and bracken in deciduous and coniferous woodland on acid soil. Occurs late summer to autumn.

Porcelain Mushroom

Oudemansiella mucida

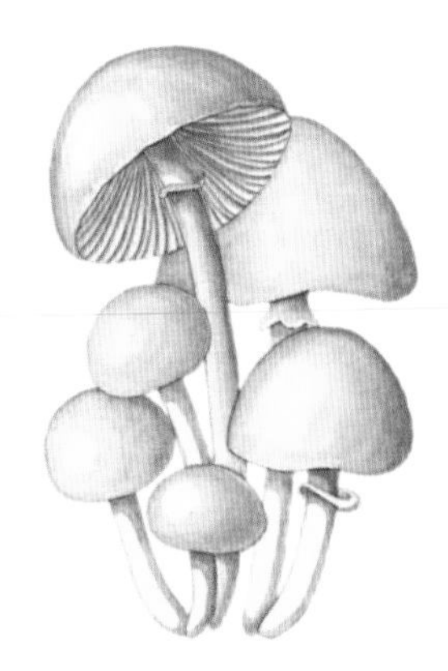

Cap to 10cm; stem to 10cm. Medium-sized all-white fungus. Cap slimy and semi-translucent. Gills white or ivory; free. Stem length varies considerably as it rises to clear the cap from the tree on which it grows; slightly scaly and carries a membranous ring. Grows in clusters both on fallen branches and high up in beech trees. Common species. Occurs late summer to early winter.

Rooting Shank

Xerula radicata

Cap to 10cm; stem to 20cm. Cap pale to dark brown, radially furrowed; first convex or bell shaped, then flatter and usually umbonate. Gills white; free. Flesh white. Stem length is twice the width of the cap; white shading into brown at the base. If carefully dug up, a long extension of the stem, which attaches it to buried wood, can be seen. Usually grows parasitically on beech and hazel stumps, roots and buried wood, both singly and in small groups. Widespread and common in southern England, often on chalk. Occurs midsummer to autumn.

Fairy Ring Champignon

Marasmius oreades

Size and description Cap to 5cm; stem to 9cm. Cap tan; convex, then flatter with a broad umbo. Gills white; widely spaced and adnate. Flesh white. Stem similar in colour to the cap. Like other species in this genus, the fungus has the ability to dry out and later rehydrate without deteriorating.

Habitat Grows in rings on cultivated lawns and pastures, often in large numbers. Widespread and common across Europe.

Season Spring to autumn.

St George's Mushroom

Calocybe gambosa

Size and description
Cap to 12cm; stem to 8cm. Medium and stout, resembling a cultivated mushroom. Cap whitish-cream, often with a brownish tinge; convex to flattish with an incurved wavy margin. Gills white or cream; crowded and adnate. Flesh thick. Smells strongly of new meal. Stem whitish and smooth.

Habitat Grows in clumps and large rings on chalky soil in pastures, mixed woodland and hedgerows. Widespread but uncommon, with an uneven distribution across Europe.

Season Spring to early summer.

Plums and Custard

Tricholomopsis rutilans

SIZE AND DESCRIPTION Cap to 10cm; stem to 10cm. Cap yellow, but the colour is almost completely obscured by a layer of red-brown scales; conical or convex, then flatter, often with a broad umbo and incurved margins. Gills bright egg-yolk yellow; adnate. Flesh cream. Stem paler than the cap.

HABITAT Grows on and around conifer stumps and fallen trees. Common and widespread across Europe.

SEASON Late autumn to early winter.

Broad Gill

Megacollybia platyphylla

Size and description Cap to 15cm; stem to 15cm. Cap greyish-brown with radiating fibrils. Gills greyish-white and broad; adnate. Flesh white. Stem white or greyish-brown, covered with brownish mycelia strands resembling rootlets. If the fungus is carefully dug up it can be seen to have long white mycelial cords attached to the base of the stem.

Habitat Grows on the decayed wood of mainly deciduous trees, or from buried wood under the ground. Infrequent but locally common.

Season Summer to autumn.

Changeable Melanoleuca

Melanoleuca melaleuca

Size and description Cap to 8cm; stem to 7cm. Cap dark brown, turning paler with age; at first flattened convex, then becoming umbonate. Gills white; sinuate. Flesh white. Stem white with greyish fibrils, becoming darker with age, so retaining contrast with the cap throughout the life of the fungus.

Habitat Generally grows either in small troops or singly in grassy pasture, lawns near trees and grass in open deciduous woodland. Common species.

Season Late summer to autumn.

Wood Blewit

Lepista nuda

Size and description Cap to 15cm; stem to 10cm. The whole fungus – cap, adnate gills and stem when young and fresh – is bluish-lilac, but the surface of the cap rapidly fades and becomes almost buff. Cap initially convex with a broad umbo, later depressed with an irregular wavy margin. Stem tends to broaden towards the base.

Habitat Grows in troops and rings in deciduous and coniferous woodland, parkland and gardens. Very common across Europe.

Season Late autumn to early winter.

Field Blewit

Lepista saeva

Size and description Cap to 12cm; stem to 10cm. Cap pale tan; initially convex, then flatter, depressed and undulating. Gills concolorous with the cap; adnate. Stem lilac, unchanging, usually swollen. Aroma perfumed, strong and pleasant – perhaps the most distinguishing feature.

Habitat Occurs in groups that often form rings, sometimes in very large numbers, in pasture and other grassy areas. Widespread across Europe, but not common. Occasionally found in England.

Season Late autumn to early winter.

Heath Naval

Lichenomphalia umbellifera

Size and description Cap to 2cm; stem to 2cm. Cap off-white, becoming yellowish or pale brown with age; characteristically funnel shaped, giving rise to the common name. Gills pale yellowish-cream; spaced and markedly decurrent. Stem thin and similar in colour to the cap.

Habitat Occurs on acid peaty soil in moss and lichens, and on rotten wood. The fruit body of the fungus component of a small green lichen, *Botrydina vulgaris*, which occurs on damp peaty soil. In Britain common in Scotland, and occasionally found elsewhere.

Season Early summer to late autumn.

Sprucecone Cap

Strobilurus esculentus

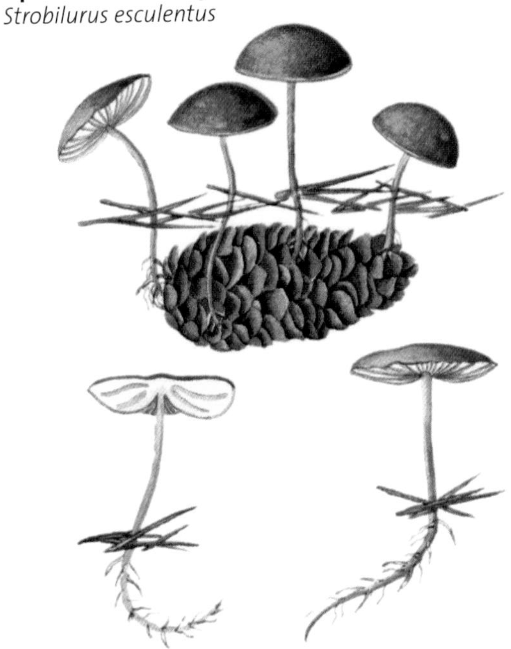

Size and description Cap to 2.5cm; stem to 7cm. Cap pale greyish-white to mid-brown; initially convex, later becoming flatter. Gills whitish; almost free. Stem rather thin, similar in colour to the cap.

Habitat Grows on spruce cones, usually those that are partly buried in the ground or partially decayed.

Season Spring.

The Goblet

Pseudoclitocybe cyathiformis

Size and description
Cap to 8cm; stem to 10cm. Cap dark greyish-brown; initially convex with a depressed centre, then deeply funnel shaped. Gills greyish, turning brown with age and extending onto the stem. Flesh pallid. Stem greyish-brown with a silky white fibrous covering, and swollen towards the base.

Habitat Grows singly or in small groups in mixed woodland among grass, leaf litter and other debris, particularly in damp locations. Widespread in Europe, but not common.

Season Late autumn to winter.

Giant Funnel

Leucopaxillus giganteus

Size and description Cap to 30cm; stem to 7cm. Funnel with a very large cap and relatively short stem. Cap whitish in colour; funnel shaped, and often cracked or scaly. Gills whitish; crowded and decurrent. Flesh hard and white with a sweet odour. Stem stout and whitish with a bulbous base.

Habitat Grows in groups, often forming rings, in grass in pastures, hedgerows and woodland clearings. Widespread in Europe, but nowhere common.

Bitter Oysterling

Panellus stipticus

Size and description Cap to 4cm; stem to 2cm. Small and thin-fleshed, shell-shaped bracket fungus. Cap pale cinnamon-brown; thin with incurved margins and sometimes concentrically zoned. Gills darker than the cap; crowded, narrow, and adnate or decurrent. Stem very short and stout, lateral and attached to the cap on one side.

Habitat Grows in tiered clusters on dead deciduous wood, with often 20–30 or more in a group; favours oaks. Often grows on the cut edges of sawn trunks and logs. Common, especially late in season.

Season Late autumn to winter.

Velvet Shank

Flammulina velutipes

Size and description Cap to 10cm; stem to 10cm. Cap light orange, darker towards the centre; flat, and slimy when wet. Gills pale yellow; broad and quite crowded. Flesh yellow on the cap and dark brown on the stem. Stem concolorous with the cap at the apex, dark chocolate-brown and velvety-brown below, often curved and very tough. Edible and widely cultivated in the Far East.

Habitat Occurs in clusters on decaying deciduous trees, particularly oaks and elms. Widespread and common in Europe.

Season Autumn to winter.

Livid Pinkgill

Entoloma sinuatum

Size and description Cap to 20cm; stem to 10cm. Cap creamy-white to pale greyish-ochre; initially convex, then flatter and sometimes wavy at the edge. Gills start white and become yellowish salmon-pink as coloured spores develop; adnate. Flesh white, fairly thick. Stem concolorous with the cap. Poisonous: in Europe often confused with edible mushrooms such as St George's Mushroom (page 72) and The Miller (opposite). Also called Livid Agaric and Lead Poisoner.

Habitat Grows in deciduous woodland under oaks, beeches and less commonly birches, often on clay soils; also found in parks. Occurs throughout Europe to Britain and Ireland, but more common in southern and central parts of Europe than in north-west.

Season Late summer to autumn.

The Miller

Clitopilus prunulus

Size and description Cap to 10cm; stem to 4cm. Cap creamy-white with a distinctive soft velvety texture; convex at first, becoming flattened with a depressed centre and wavy margin. Gills white at first, becoming pale pink at maturity; crowded and decurrent. Flesh firm and white with a strong odour of meal. Stem concolorous with the cap and covered in fine down.

Habitat Grows in scattered groups on rich soil in grass in open woodland. Widespread throughout Europe, although it has an uneven distribution.

Season Midsummer to late autumn.

Deer Shield

Pluteus cervinus

Size and description Cap to 12cm; stem to 10cm. Cap varying shades of brown; initially bell shaped, then convex or flatter, generally with a broad umbo. Gills white, though the pink colour of the spores shows in the spaces between them; crowded and free. Flesh white. Stem white with brownish fibrils.

Habitat Grows in scattered groups on the stumps and trunks of deciduous trees, and on sawdust heaps and other woody debris. Very common and widespread in Europe.

Season Early spring to early winter.

Goldleaf Shield

Pluteus romellii

Size and description Cap to 4cm; stem to 7cm. Cap smooth and cinnamon-brown, becoming yellowish at the margins; convex at first, becoming flattened at maturity. Gills whitish at first, then chrome-yellow and finally pink; free. Flesh yellowish and thin. Stem yellow and slender.

Habitat Grows singly or in small clumps on the logs, wood chips and other woody debris of deciduous trees, especially beeches. Found across Europe, but quite rare and has an uneven distribution.

Season Spring to early winter.

Velvet Shield

Pluteus umbrosus

SIZE AND DESCRIPTION Cap to 9cm; stem to 9cm. Cap brown with velvety black scales; initially convex, then flatter and umbonate with an incurved margin. Gills pink with dark brown edges; crowded and free. Flesh thin, soft and white with an odour of garlic. Stem cylindrical; similar surface to the cap.

HABITAT Occurs in small groups on the stumps, rotten wood and debris of deciduous trees, particularly beeches, ashes and elms. Widespread in Europe, but patchily distributed and quite rare.

SEASON Late summer to autumn.

Veined Shield

Pluteus petasatus

Size and description Cap to 14cm; stem to 10cm. Cap whitish with dark brown scales concentrated at the centre; initially convex, then flatter and umbonate. Gills white, maturing to greyish-pink; crowded and free. Flesh white and soft with an odour of radishes. Stem thick and whitish with brown or blackish fibres at the base.

Habitat Occurs in clumps on the stumps, debris and sawdust of deciduous trees. Fairly widespread in Europe, but nowhere common.

Season Early summer to late autumn.

Stubble Rosegill

Volvariella gloiocephala

Size and description Cap to 12cm; stem to 16cm. Cap white with a darker centre; oval when young, expanding to convex and flattened at maturity, usually with a broad umbo. Gills white, turning to pink at maturity, crowded and free. Flesh white and firm with an earthy odour. Stem whitish, smooth and tapered, arising from a sac-like white volva with no ring.

Habitat Grows in scattered groups, sometimes in large numbers, on compost heaps, manured ground, dung heaps, rotted straw and stubble fields. Common and widespread in Europe, but with a patchy distribution.

Season Summer to early winter.

Silky Rosegill
Volvariella bombycina

Size and description Cap to 20cm; stem to 15cm. Cap white; bell shaped, covered with silky fibres. Gills pink, crowded and free. Stem smooth and white, arising from a sac-like brownish volva with no ring.
Habitat Grows singly on the decayed stumps or standing trunks of deciduous trees, particularly elms. Widespread but rare in Europe.
Season Early spring to late autumn.

Webcap species

Cortinarius mucifluoides

Size and description Cap to 10cm; stem to 10cm. Cap rich brown, paler and striate on the outer third, and slimy; initially hemispherical or convex, then flatter with a broad umbo. Gills rusty coloured; adnate or free. Flesh pale brown. Stem slimy, slightly swollen in the middle; white with a slimy violet veil to the ring zone. One of numerous species of *Cortinarius*, many poisonous, and few of which can be recognized in the field.

Habitat Grows mainly in deciduous woodland, especially on beeches. Widespread and common.

Season Autumn.

Deadly Webcap

Cortinarius rubellus

Size and description Cap to 7cm; stem to 10cm. Cap tawny to date-brown, darker in the centre, and dry and fibrous; initially conical, then flatter. Gills and flesh initially ochre-brown, then rust-brown with paler edges; adnate. Stem tall, colour similar to the cap, dry and fibrous. Spores rusty coloured. Deadly: can destroy the kidneys (symptoms are late in onset), and accounts for about 4 per cent of fungus fatalities. Particularly dangerous due to its similarity to the edible chanterelles.

Habitat Grows under pines, with a northern distribution in Europe. Rare in Britain, where it is found mainly in Scotland. Similar species grow under deciduous trees in southerly areas; all are poisonous.

Season Autumn.

Spectacular Rustgill

Gymnopilus junonius

Size and description Cap to 15cm; stem to 15cm. Large tufted species. Cap deep golden-yellow; initially convex, then flatter and generally broadly umbonate. Gills yellow and coloured by rusty spores that fall on the stem; adnate. Flesh yellow. Stem concolorous with the cap, and stout and swollen towards the base, with an ascending ring.

Habitat Grows on decayed deciduous wood, often buried and arising from buried roots and wood, so that it appears to be growing on the ground. Widespread and common.

Season Summer to early winter.

Poison Pie

Hebeloma crustuliniforme

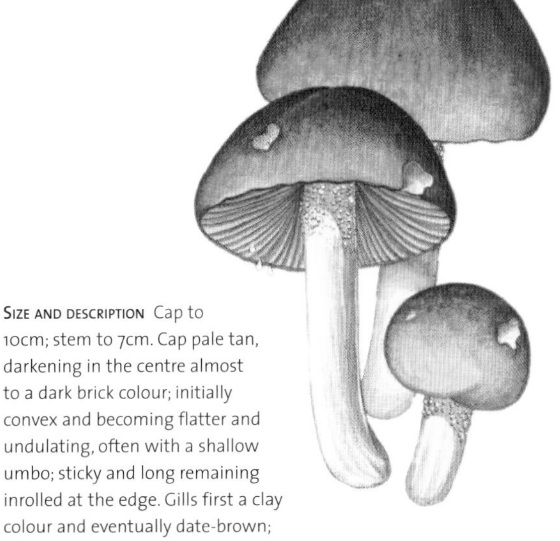

Size and description Cap to 10cm; stem to 7cm. Cap pale tan, darkening in the centre almost to a dark brick colour; initially convex and becoming flatter and undulating, often with a shallow umbo; sticky and long remaining inrolled at the edge. Gills first a clay colour and eventually date-brown; adnate. In wet weather the gills develop drops of water on the edges, which catch the spores and dry to leave brown spots. Flesh white and thick. Stem pale whitish-fawn. Smells strongly of radishes. Poisonous, causing gastric upsets.

Habitat Grows singly or in groups along wood edges, under trees and on lawns. Widespread and common.

Season Autumn.

Bitter Poison Pie

Hebeloma sinapizans

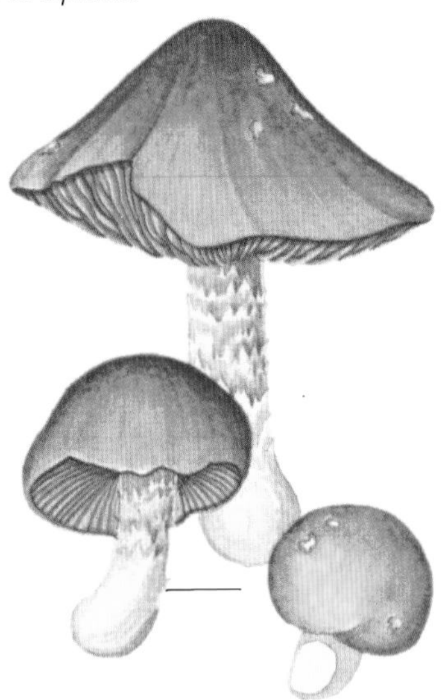

Size and description Cap to 12cm; stem to 12cm. Cap yellowish-clay, darkening in time to pale tan, and sticky; initially convex, then flatter and undulating, sometimes with a shallow umbo. Gills cinnamon-brown and spores rusty; crowded and adnate. Flesh white. Stem pale, sturdy and has a basal swelling. Smells strongly of radishes or raw potatoes.

Habitat Grows in deciduous and mixed woodland. Widespread although infrequent.

Season Autumn.

Split Fibrecap

Inocybe rimosa

Size and description Cap to 7cm; stem to 8cm. Common but variable fibrecap. Cap yellowish with darker brown silky radiating fibres; similar to a bell tent in shape. The radial cracks in the cap are a distinguishing feature. Gills dirty yellow with a white edge; crowded and adnate. Stem even, fairly tall and slim, and similar in colour to the cap.
Habitat Grows under deciduous trees, especially beeches. Widespread and common.
Season Early summer to late autumn.

White Fibrecap

Inocybe geophylla

Size and description Cap to 4cm; stem to 6cm. Cap white with a smooth and silky surface; at first conical, then as it opens out becoming bell shaped or flatter with a pronounced umbo. Gills at first whitish, then clay coloured; spores rusty; gills almost free. Flesh white. Stem whitish, cylindrical, fairly long in relation to the cap and often bent.

Habitat Occurs singly or in troops in all types of woodland, and sometimes also in mossy lawns. Common along path edges in woodland.

Season Early summer to late autumn.

Deadly Fibrecap

Inocybe erubescens

Size and description Cap to 8cm; stem to 10cm. Cap ivory with red radial fibres, and silky; initially conical, then bell shaped or flatter, generally with a broad umbo. Gills at first pink, then grey-brown, bruising red; adnate. Stem stout, ivory coloured as the cap, with longitudinal red fibrils. All parts bruise red. Deadly poisonous: even in small quantities, causes death from heart failure or asphyxiation.

Habitat Characteristically found singly or in troops on chalk in beech woods. Infrequent.

Season Late spring to autumn.

Brown Rollrim

Paxillus involutus

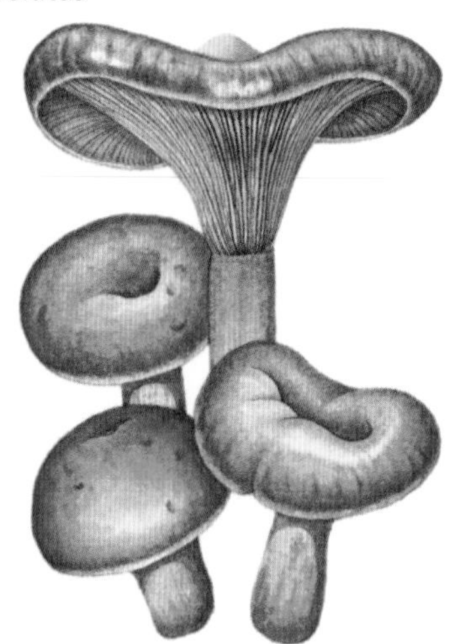

Size and description Cap to 12cm; stem to 7cm. Medium-sized species related to the boletes (pages 10–24). Cap downy brown; maintains an inrolled margin for a long time, then becomes funnel shaped and reveals the decurrent ochre gills. These are readily pushed off the stem with a fingernail. Flesh and stem similar in colour to the cap. Stem stout and cylindrical or sometimes slightly thicker at the base, and covered with longitudinal fibrils.

Habitat Occurs singly or in troops in deciduous woodland, where it is usually associated with birches, and on acid heaths. Widespread and common.

Season Late summer to autumn.

Yellow Fieldcap

Bolbitius titubans

Size and description Cap to 4cm; stem to 8cm. Cap bright yellow; initially oval, then bell shaped and finally flattish; at first viscid, then furrowed and splitting at the margin. Gills at first yellowish, then becoming rusty; crowded and adnate. Stem tall, cylindrical and slim, tending to thicken at the base, and creamy at first covered with a pale meal.

Habitat Grows on dung, woodchip mulch or rotting straw, or in grass enriched by dung. Widespread and common.

Season Late summer to autumn.

Sulphur Tuft

Hypholoma fasciculare

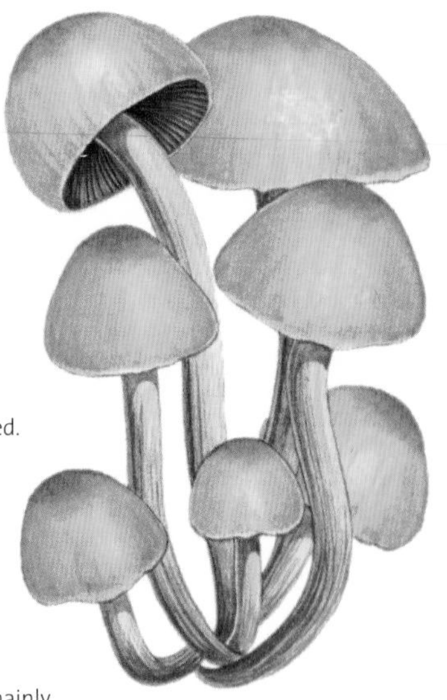

Size and description Cap to 7cm; stem to 9cm. Cap surface smooth and sulphur-yellow, developing a green tint, then blackening; initially convex, then flatter and often umbonate. Gills yellowish-green, then purple-black; crowded and adnate. Flesh yellowish. Stem coloured as the cap, cylindrical and usually curved. Grows in dense tufts, the lower caps becoming discoloured from the black spores of those above.
Habitat Occurs on dead wood of any type. Widespread and common.
Season All year, but found mainly summer and autumn.

Conifer Tuft

Hypholoma capnoides

Size and description Cap to 6cm; stem to 7cm. Cap pale ochre-yellow; initially convex, later becoming flatter and often umbonate, with a wavy margin. Gills bluish-grey, darkening to purplish-brown; crowded and adnate. Flesh yellow. Stem long and cylindrical, and often bent; buff with yellowish tinges and a darker brown base.

Habitat Grows in tufts on decayed conifer wood. Northerly distribution in Europe; uncommon.

Season Spring to late autumn.

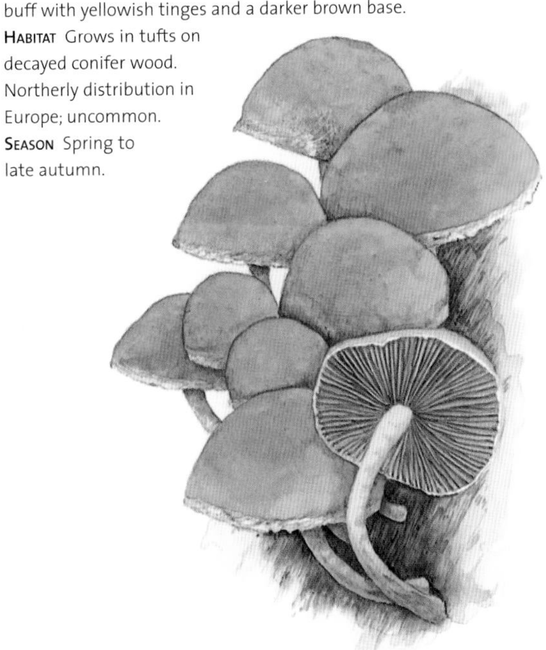

Sheathed Woodtuft

Kuehneromyces mutabilis

Size and description
Cap to 6cm; stem to 8cm. Cap smooth tan when wet, drying out from the centre to a pale ochre-yellow, giving a two-toned appearance; convex expanding to flattish umbonate. Gills pale ochre, becoming cinnamon-brown when mature. Flesh cinnamon-brown. Stem pale tan and smooth above the short-lived ring, darker below with fine dark scales that become denser and almost black at the base. Also called Brown Stew Fungus.

Habitat Grows in dense tufts on the stumps and logs of deciduous trees, particularly birches and beeches. Widespread and common throughout northern Europe.

Season Early summer to late autumn.

Shaggy Scalycap

Pholiota squarrosa

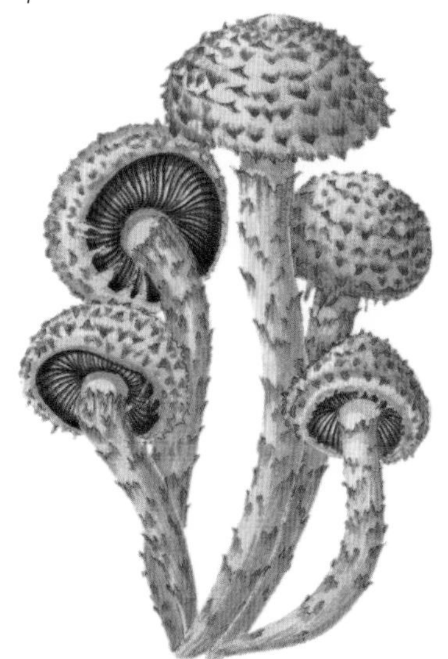

Size and description Cap to 11cm; stem to 15cm. Cap deep yellow and covered in dark brown scales; initially convex, then becoming flatter. Gills yellow, shedding rusty-brown spores; crowded and adnate. Stem long in relation to cap size, and concolorous with the cap; brown scales below ring area.

Habitat Grows in dense tufts at the bases of living deciduous trees, particularly beeches and rowans, and also occasionally conifers. Occurs infrequently.

Season Late summer to autumn.

Dung Roundhead

Stropharia semiglobata

Size and description Cap to 4cm; stem to 10cm. Cap pale yellow; slimy and hemispherical, sometimes with a barely defined umbo. Gills black; wide and adnate. Stem very slender and smooth, similar in colour to the cap and carrying a slight black ring.

Habitat Grows in small troops on and near to dung, especially that of herbivores, and occasionally on manured grassland.

Season Late spring to late autumn.

Verdigris Toadstool

Stropharia aeruginosa

Size and description Cap to 8cm; stem to 10cm. Cap characteristically coloured verdigris green, and slimy; convex at first, then flatter with a broad shallow umbo. Gills initially white but become grey, then purplish-black; adnate to sinuate. Flesh bluish-white. Stem white, squamulose, with a small but definite ring that catches the spores and becomes black. Poisonous: off-putting colour signals that it is inedible.

Habitat Grows in small troops among grass in woodland, pasture and heaths. Widespread.

Season Midsummer to autumn.

Magic Mushroom

Psilocybe semilanceata

Size and description Cap to 1.5cm; stem to 7.5cm. Cap a characteristic bonnet shape with an incurved margin; yellowish-cream, smooth and sticky when damp. Gills light brown maturing to dark brown; adnate. Stem long and very thin, and pale buff in colour. Poisonous: its hallucinogenic properties have given it the name Magic Mushroom, and it is now illegal to possess it. Also called Liberty Cap.

Habitat Occurs in scattered troops in short grass everywhere. Infrequent but locally common.

Season Summer to autumn.

Petticoat Mottlegill

Panaeolus papilionaceus

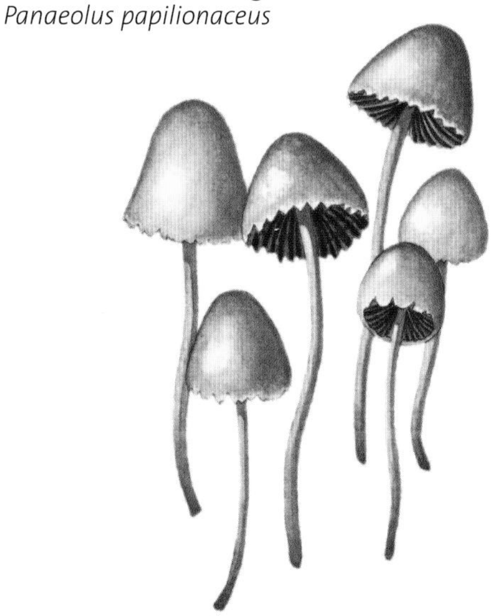

Size and description Cap to 4cm; stem to 12cm. Small species that undergoes an extreme change of colour as it dries. Cap blackish-brown when young, changing to a pale creamy-ochre, darker in the centre; conical or convex at first, then bell shaped, sometimes umbonate; margin when fresh has a frill of white fibres. Gills black; adnate. Stem also changes colour as it dries, from dark brown to cream at the apex.

Habitat Grows in troops in rich grassland, often on or near dung. Widespread and common.

Season Early summer to autumn.

Egghead Mottlegill

Panaeolus semiovatus

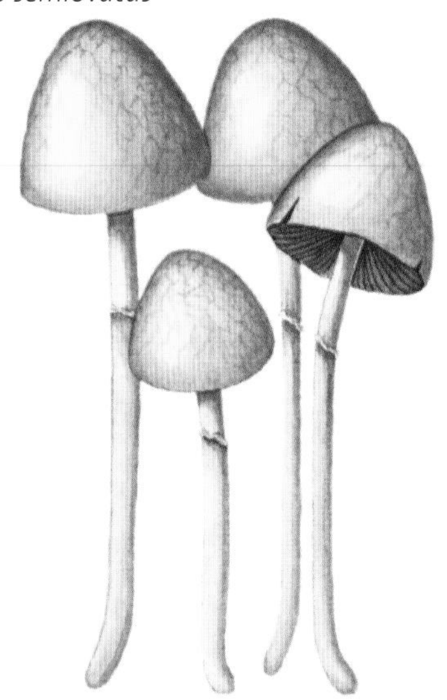

Size and description Cap to 6cm; stem to 15cm. Cap pale clay in colour with a yellow tinge towards the centre, the shape of half an oval; greasy on the surface when moist, and shiny and wrinkled when dry. Gills black and unevenly spotted with white-fringed edges; adnate. Flesh pale and slight. Stem concolorous with the cap, tall and slim with a fibrous black ring.

Habitat Grows in troops in horse and cow dung, and in manure in gardens. Widespread and common.

Season Summer to early winter.

Parasol

Macrolepiota procera

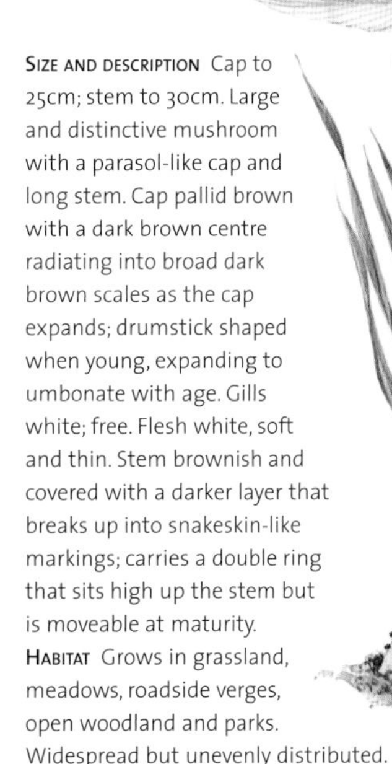

Size and description Cap to 25cm; stem to 30cm. Large and distinctive mushroom with a parasol-like cap and long stem. Cap pallid brown with a dark brown centre radiating into broad dark brown scales as the cap expands; drumstick shaped when young, expanding to umbonate with age. Gills white; free. Flesh white, soft and thin. Stem brownish and covered with a darker layer that breaks up into snakeskin-like markings; carries a double ring that sits high up the stem but is moveable at maturity.
Habitat Grows in grassland, meadows, roadside verges, open woodland and parks. Widespread but unevenly distributed.
Season Midsummer to late autumn.

Parasol species

Macrolepiota excoriata

Size and description Cap to 10cm; stem to 7cm. Cap white with pale buff scales; convex at first, later flattish with a frayed margin. Gills white or cream; crowded and free from the stem. Flesh white and soft. Stem white with a thin, tightly attached ring bearing a fringed brownish margin.

Habitat Only grows in pastureland, particularly water meadows. Widespread but patchy in Europe. Rare in Britain, but grows abundantly on the Somerset Levels.

Season Late summer to late autumn.

Slender Parasol

Macrolepiota mastoidea

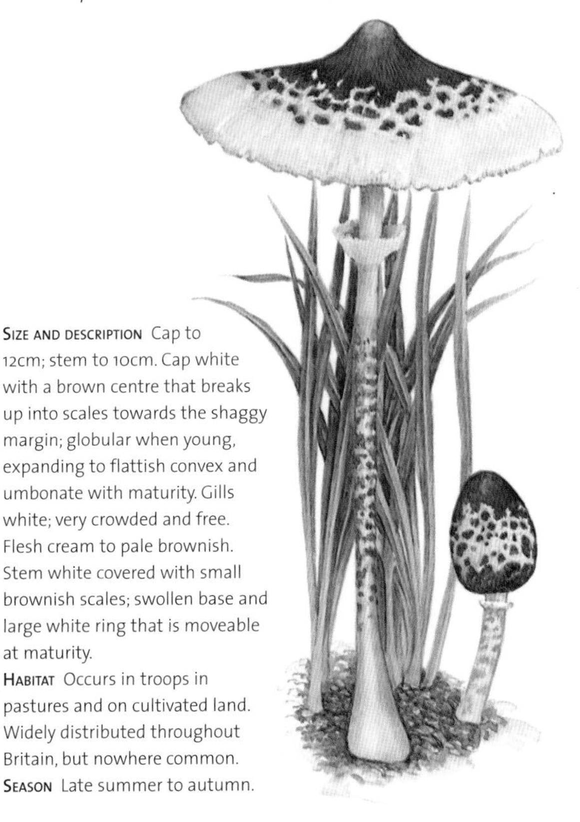

Size and description Cap to 12cm; stem to 10cm. Cap white with a brown centre that breaks up into scales towards the shaggy margin; globular when young, expanding to flattish convex and umbonate with maturity. Gills white; very crowded and free. Flesh cream to pale brownish. Stem white covered with small brownish scales; swollen base and large white ring that is moveable at maturity.

Habitat Occurs in troops in pastures and on cultivated land. Widely distributed throughout Britain, but nowhere common.

Season Late summer to autumn.

Stinking Parasol

Lepiota cristata

Size and description Cap to 4cm; stem to 5cm. Cap white covered with reddish-brown scales that are dense in the centre and absent towards the edge; initially hemispherical, later convex to flat with a blunt umbo. Gills white; crowded and free. Flesh white. Stem slightly yellow or brown, with a white or brownish ring. Strong and unpleasant smell.
Habitat Grows in deciduous woodland, gardens and pastures. Widespread and very common – the most common parasol.
Season Late summer to autumn.

Shaggy Parasol

Chlorophyllum rhacodes

Size and description Cap to 18cm; stem to 15cm. Resembles Parasol (page 111), but is stouter and has more shaggy scales on the cap. Cap pale buff to cinnamon-brown, breaking up to form fibrous shaggy scales as the cap expands, showing white flesh beneath; egg shaped when young, expanding to convex to flattish with age. Gills white; crowded and free. Flesh thick and white, reddening in stem when cut. Stem white tinged pinkish-brown, smooth and with a two-tiered white ring that is moveable at maturity.

Habitat Grows singly or in scattered groups in coniferous and deciduous woodland, and in hedgerows. Widespread but unevenly distributed in Europe.

Season Midsummer to late autumn.

Earthy Powdercap

Cystoderma amianthinum

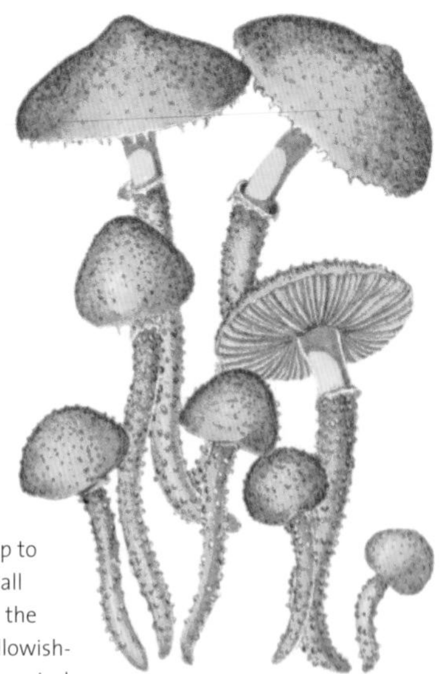

Size and description Cap to 5cm; stem to 5cm. Small fungus at one time in the *Lepiota* genus. Cap yellowish-tan and scaly; initially conical, then flattened and sometimes umbonate. Gills white or cream; adnate. Flesh white. Stem white above the immoveable ring, but both the underside of the ring and the entire stem below it are covered with scales similar in colour to the cap.

Habitat Mainly a heathland species. Widespread and common.

Season Late summer to autumn.

Yellow-staining Mushroom

Agaricus xanthodermus

Size and description Cap to 10cm; stem to 10cm. Cap white bruising to yellow, with a similar shape to that of edible Field Mushroom (page 118). Gills whitish to pale pink, becoming grey then black; adnate to free. Flesh at the base of the stem discolours yellow when cut. Stem with a large floppy ring. Smell unpleasant, carbolic. Poisonous: can cause severe digestive disturbances in some people.

Habitat Grows in woods, meadows and gardens. Widespread and common species.

Season Summer to autumn.

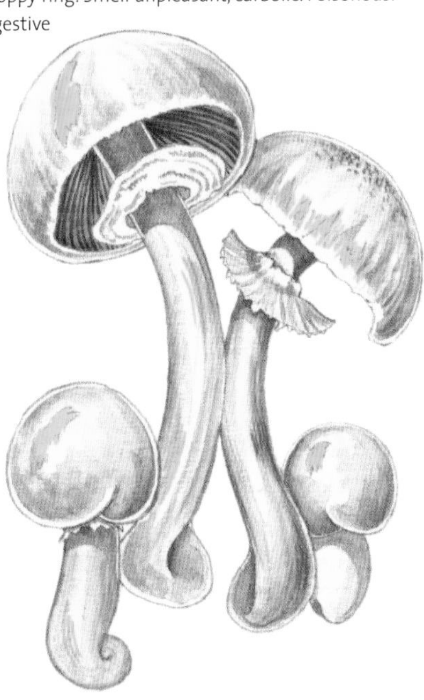

Field Mushroom

Agaricus campestris

Size and description Cap to 10cm; stem to 8cm. Familiar medium-sized sturdy mushroom. Cap creamy-white with variable brownish scales on the surface. Gills start pink before becoming chocolate-brown or blackish at maturity; adnate. Flesh white. Stem white with a ring.

Habitat Grows in groups, which are occasionally very large after rain, on chalky soil among grass, and in meadows and pastures. Quite common in Europe, but declining.

Season Midsummer to late autumn.

The Prince

Agaricus augustus

Size and description Cap to 25cm; stem to 20cm. Cap chestnut-brown at first, becoming patterned with fibrous scales in concentric rings on a yellow-tinged background as the cap expands; initially ovoid, then convex with a flattened centre. Gills pale pink, becoming chocolate-brown or blackish; crowded and free. Flesh white, bruising yellow, with a strong odour of bitter almonds. Stem white above ring, which is persistent, large and hanging; scaly below, penetrating deep into substrate.

Habitat Grows in clumps or clusters on rich soil in deciduous and coniferous woodland, hedges and gardens. Widespread across Europe, but nowhere common.

Season Late summer to autumn.

Wood Mushroom

Agaricus silvicola

Size and description Cap to 18cm; stem to 10cm. Cap cream bruising yellowish, smooth and shining; egg shaped at first, then convex and eventually almost flat. Gills pinkish-grey, becoming chocolate-brown to black at maturity; crowded and free. Flesh thin and white with an odour of aniseed. Stem concolourous with the cap; slightly bulbous base and a large ring.

Habitat Grows in troops on soil in coniferous and deciduous woodland. Widespread in Europe, but occasional.

Season Late summer to autumn.

Horse Mushroom

Agaricus arvensis

Size and description
Cap to 15cm; stem to 12cm. Cap ivory-white bruising yellow, mealy when young, then silky. Gills white at first, becoming greyish-pink, then black; adnate and almost free. Flesh thick, firm and white with a strong odour of aniseed. Stem stout, carrying a thick, cogwheel-like ring.

Habitat Grows in cultivated fields, often in large 'fairy' rings. Widespread but unevenly distributed in Europe.

Season Early summer to late autumn.

Macro Mushroom

Agaricus urinascens

Size and description Cap to 30cm; stem to 12cm. Cap whitish; deeply domed, eventually expanding to become convex, and splitting into woolly or scaly patches. Gills whitish-grey turning pink and finally brown; crowded and free. Flesh firm and white with an odour of aniseed that becomes unpleasant with age. Stem creamy white with a tapering base; lower half covered with thick scales.
Habitat Grows in rings in nutrient-rich pastures, particularly on calcareous soil. Widespread but uncommon across Europe.
Season Early to late summer.

Scaly Wood Mushroom

Agaricus silvaticus

Size and description Cap to 10cm; stem to 12cm. Cap brownish; button-like at first, expanding to convex with a pattern of flaky fibrous scales against a whitish background. Gills pale pink at first, and becoming reddish, then chocolate-brown when mature; free. Flesh firm and white, becoming red and finally dark brown when cut. Stem whitish above a pendulous brownish ring and scaly below, with a slightly bulbous base. Also called Red-staining Mushroom.

Habitat Occurs in troops on rich soils in woodland, particularly under conifers, favouring spruce. Quite common and widespread across Europe.

Season Late summer to autumn.

Pavement Mushroom

Agaricus bitorquis

Size and description Cap to 12cm; stem to 8cm. Cap pale greyish-brown; broadly convex to flattish. Gills dull pink becoming clay coloured, then chocolate-brown; crowded and free. Flesh white tinged with pink where cut, with a sour odour. Stem thick, white and smooth with two separate sheathing rings, the lower one thinner.

Habitat Grows in trooping groups on sandy soil, particularly compacted ground in urban areas, and by roadsides. Fairly common and widespread across Europe.

Season Spring to autumn.

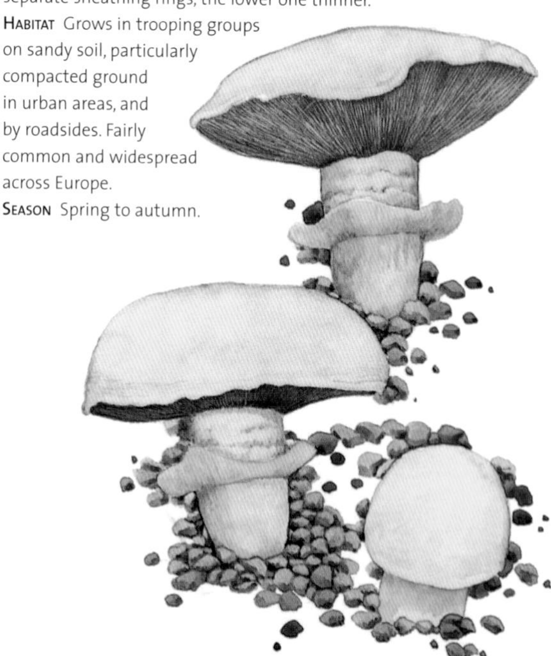

Shaggy Inkcap

Coprinus comatus

Size and description Cap to 12cm; stem to 30cm. Cap white, becoming brown on top; oval; hairy-scaly with hairs turning outwards at an intermediate stage. Gills becoming black with spores and liquefying so that the spores are spread by rain; crowded and free. Flesh white when young. Stem tall, white when young, with a persistent mobile white ring, often blackened with falling spores. Also called Lawyer's Wig.

Habitat Grows in small tufts or troops on grass verges, lawns, fallow fields, compost heaps and disturbed ground. Common and widespread across Europe.

Season Early spring to late autumn.

Common Inkcap

Coprinopsis atramentaria

Size and description Cap to 7cm; stem to 17cm. Cap greyish-brown or brown turning black; egg shaped and furrowed; margin becomes uplifted and split. Gills white becoming black and liquefying into 'ink', which was once used for writing; free. Stem tall and fairly slim.

Habitat Grows in a wide variety of habitats, and is capable of pushing its way through paths and paving. Occurs in large clusters and troops. Common and widespread in Europe, with an uneven distribution.

Season Midsummer to early winter.

Fairy Inkcap

Coprinellus disseminatus

Size and description Cap to 1.2cm; stem to 4cm. Cap creamy-buff and bell shaped, becoming greyish and convex at maturity. Gills white, becoming greyish and eventually black; crowded and free. Flesh white and fragile. Stem white and downy. Also called Trooping Crumble Cap.

Habitat Grows in massive clusters on the rotting stumps of deciduous trees. Common and widespread throughout Europe.

Season Early spring to late autumn.

Glistening Inkcap

Coprinellus micaceus

Size and description Cap to 3cm; stem to 10cm. Cap pale ochre-yellow, darker towards the centre, ornamented on top with glistening flecks of veil; soon darkens with age and loses the micaceous granules; oval when young, becoming bell shaped. Gills white, then blackening; free. Flesh whitish-grey. Stem white and smooth.

Habitat Grows on wood in dense clusters, or sometimes on the ground attached to buried wood. Common and widespread throughout Europe.

Season Spring to early winter.

Weeping Widow

Lacrymaria lacrymabunda

Size and description Cap to 10cm; stem to 10cm. Cap pale ochre-brown; convex, then flatter with a broad umbo; covered in woolly fibrils that overhang the edge as a fringe. Gills dark purplish-brown with a white edge; adnate and characteristically covered with droplets. Stem white at the top, becoming brown below the ring zone and scaly towards the base; ring short-lived and accentuated by blackish fallen spores.
Habitat Found on grassy roadsides, by paths in woodland and on roadside verges. Widespread and common.
Season Early summer to late autumn.

Branched Oyster

Pleurotus cornucopiae

SIZE AND DESCRIPTION Cap to 12cm; stem to 5cm. Medium to large bracket. Cap convex and cream coloured when young, soon becoming flattened and buffish-brown with a split and lobed margin. Gills white, maturing buff, and run down to the stem base. Flesh white and firm with a slight aniseed or meal odour. Stem whitish and usually fused with other stems in a tuft.

HABITAT Grows in dense tufts on the stumps and other wood of deciduous trees, particularly oaks, beeches and elms. Widespread but uncommon in Europe.

SEASON Late summer to autumn.

Oyster Mushroom

Pleurotus ostreatus

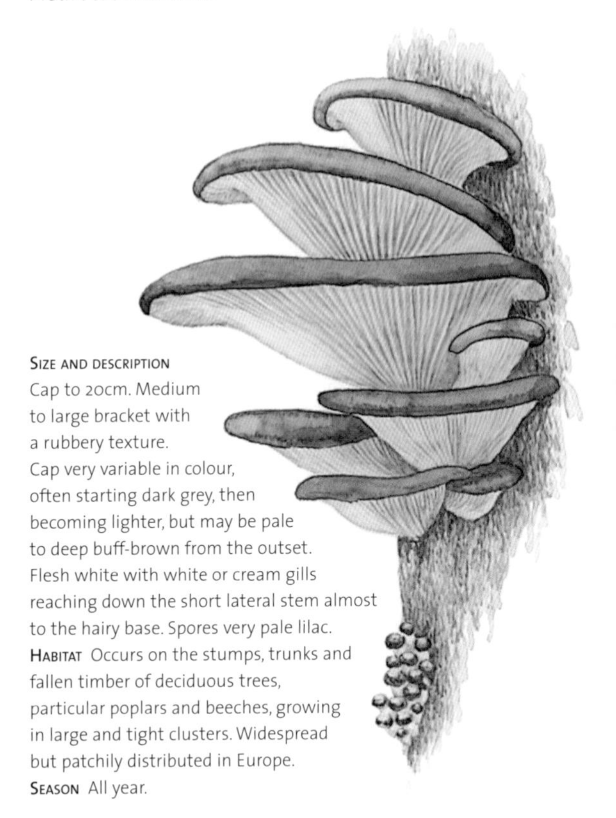

Size and description
Cap to 20cm. Medium to large bracket with a rubbery texture. Cap very variable in colour, often starting dark grey, then becoming lighter, but may be pale to deep buff-brown from the outset. Flesh white with white or cream gills reaching down the short lateral stem almost to the hairy base. Spores very pale lilac.

Habitat Occurs on the stumps, trunks and fallen timber of deciduous trees, particular poplars and beeches, growing in large and tight clusters. Widespread but patchily distributed in Europe.

Season All year.

Soft Slipper Toadstool

Crepidotus mollis

Size and description Cap to 7cm. Thin, watery and rubbery bracket. Cap pale cream and shell shaped. Gills whitish, becoming cinnamon-brown. The thin elastic skin (pellicle) on the cap top pulls off in one piece – a good diagnostic feature. Gills greyish-brown with a reddish tint, radiating outwards. Stem rudimentary or absent.

Habitat Found on the dead trunks, stumps, branches and twigs of deciduous trees. Widespread and common.

Season Early summer to late autumn.

Aniseed Cockleshell

Lentinellus cochleatus

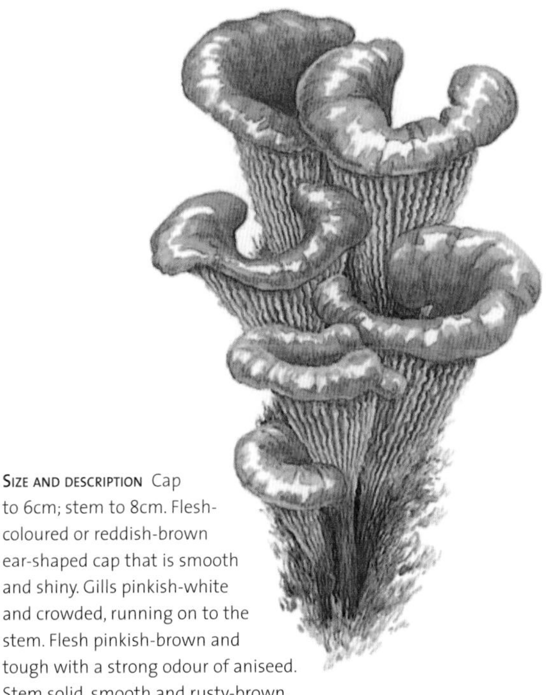

Size and description Cap to 6cm; stem to 8cm. Flesh-coloured or reddish-brown ear-shaped cap that is smooth and shiny. Gills pinkish-white and crowded, running on to the stem. Flesh pinkish-brown and tough with a strong odour of aniseed. Stem solid, smooth and rusty-brown.

Habitat Grows in large tufts on the stumps and old branches of deciduous trees. Widespread but unevenly distributed in Europe.

Season July to December.

Rosy Spike

Gomphidius roseus

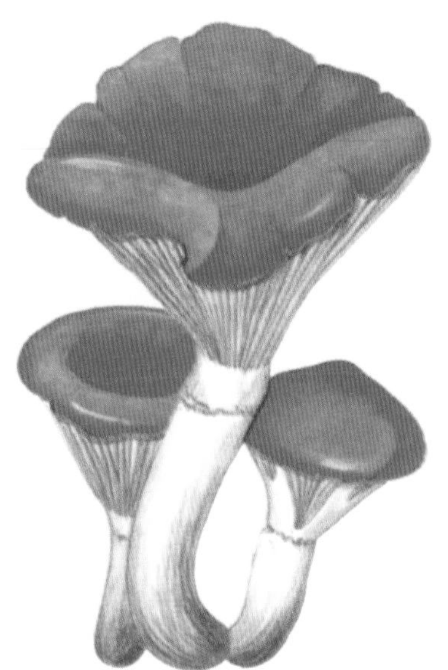

Size and description Cap to 5cm; stem to 5cm. Cap coral-pink and slimy, fading with age; convex at first, later almost flat, sometimes with a depressed centre. Gills white or pale grey; well spaced, forked and running down the stem. Spores blackish. Stem white, short and sturdy. Also called Pink Gomphidius.

Habitat Grows on acid soil with conifers and Shallow-pored Bolete (page 17), especially in grass under pines. A scarce European species.

Season Autumn.

Chanterelle

Cantharellus cibarius

Size and description Cap to 12cm; stem to 8cm. Cap pale or bright yellow fading with age; tends to become funnel shaped after starting rounded. Appears to have gills, but these are in fact branching corrugations in the spore-bearing surface, which is slightly paler than the upper surface. Stem paler than the cap, short and sturdy. Odour pleasant, reminiscent of dried apricots. Edible and of excellent flavour. Also called Chevrette and Girole. Can be confused with False Chanterelle (page 139), especially the pale variety *pallida*, but the False Chanterelle has true gills, is less chunky, does not have an aroma of apricots and grows mainly under conifers.

Habitat Grows in woodland, most commonly under beeches, birches and pines, in open mossy clearings. Widespread and quite common across Europe.

Season Early summer to early winter.

Trumpet Chanterelle

Cantharellus tubaeformis

Size and description Cap to 6cm; stem to 8cm. Cap dingy brown with a wavy irregular margin. Spore-bearing ridges beneath yellowish, becoming grey with age. Stem yellowish and hollow. Flesh tough and thin with a faint sweetish odour. Seen side on, the whole fungus looks like a tiny wind-inverted umbrella.

Habitat Grows on acid soil in deciduous and coniferous woodland, particularly on the mossy banks of woodland streams. Widespread across Europe.

Season Late summer to early winter.

Horn of Plenty

Craterellus cornucopioides

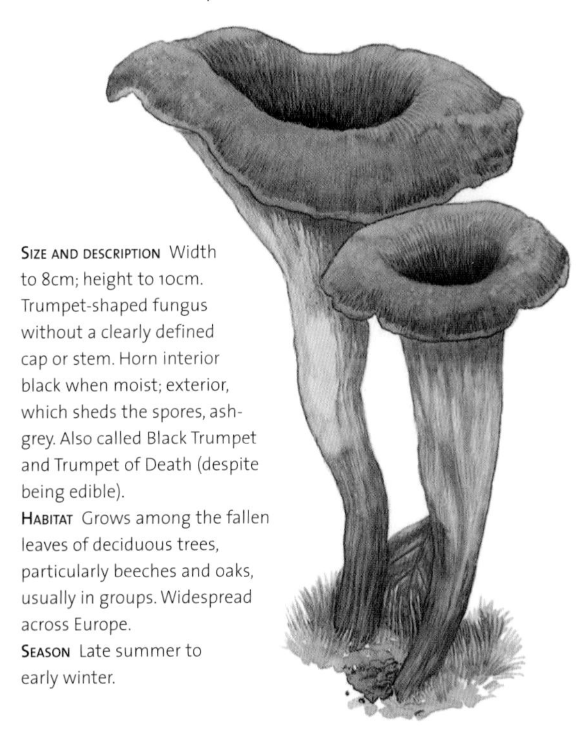

Size and description Width to 8cm; height to 10cm. Trumpet-shaped fungus without a clearly defined cap or stem. Horn interior black when moist; exterior, which sheds the spores, ash-grey. Also called Black Trumpet and Trumpet of Death (despite being edible).

Habitat Grows among the fallen leaves of deciduous trees, particularly beeches and oaks, usually in groups. Widespread across Europe.

Season Late summer to early winter.

Sinuous Chanterelle

Pseudocraterellus undulatus

Size and description Cap to 5cm; stem to 6cm. Cap greyish-brown, hollow and irregularly funnel shaped, with a crisp and frilly margin. Lower spore-bearing surface greyish-brown, and irregularly wrinkled and folded. Flesh pale with a fruity odour.

Habitat Grows in groups in soil among the leaf litter in deciduous woodland. Widespread but uncommon.

Season Midsummer to late autumn.

False Chanterelle

Hygrophoropsis aurantiaca

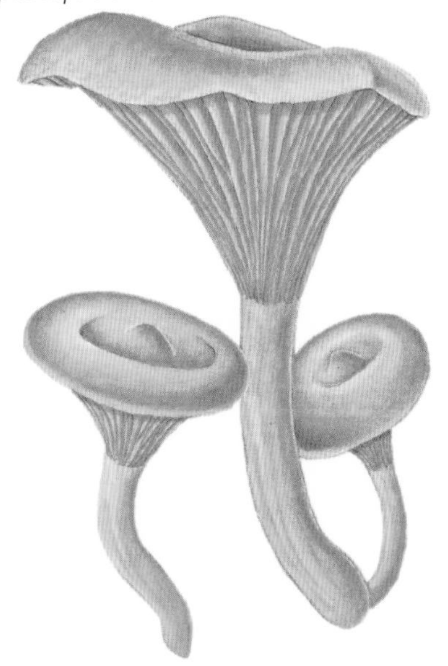

Size and description Cap to 7cm; stem to 4cm. Very similar in shape to *Clitocybe* species. Cap yellow to dark orange; convex then shallow funnel shaped with an inrolled wavy margin. Gills orange; crowded and very decurrent. Flesh and stem also orange. Not generally poisonous, but may cause hallucinations and sickness if eaten.

Habitat Grows under conifers, especially pines. Widespread and very common.

Season Late summer to late autumn.

Hen of the Woods

Grifola frondosa

Size and description Cap to 10cm; clump diameter 20–50 cm. Bracket cauliflower-like with a short central stem branching to form numerous fan-shaped brownish-olive caps, each with a crinkly dark margin and radial stripes. Spore-bearing surface underneath white. Flesh thick, white and fibrous with a sweet odour.

Habitat Occurs on the extreme bases of deciduous trees, on buried stumps and roots, favouring beeches, oaks, ash, hornbeams and Sweet Chestnuts. Widespread in Europe, but not common.

Season Late summer to autumn.

Chicken of the Woods

Laetiporus sulphureus

Size and description Fruit body 10–40cm. Bracket semicircular to fan shaped, flattened and crinkly with a thick margin, usually growing in tiered clusters. Upper surface egg-yolk yellow, darkening with age, although the margin remains bright yellow. Spore-bearing surface underneath sulphur-yellow. Flesh yellowish-orange, thick, soft and juicy, drying to white, tough and chalky.

Habitat Grows on deciduous trees, particularly oaks, Yews, Sweet Chestnuts, apples and willows. Widespread and quite common.

Season Early spring to late autumn.

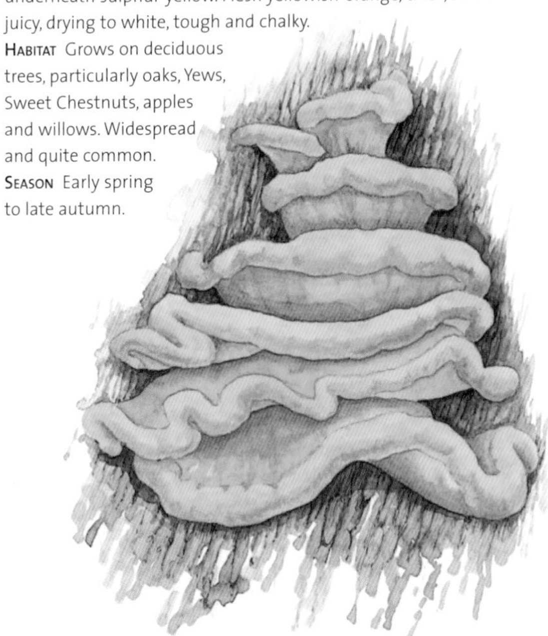

Giant Polypore

Meripilus giganteus

Fruit body 10–30cm. One of the largest polypores. Forms a rosette of fan-shaped caps, each one to 2cm thick. Felty-brown and zoned on the upper surface. Pores yellowish-grey bruising darker. Whole fruit body may measure a metre across in large specimens. Grows on the dead roots of trees, particularly beeches, appearing on the ground often at some distance from the trunk or stump. Occurs summer to early autumn.

Birch Polypore

Pitoporus betulinus

Fruit body 10–20cm. Bracket with rounded semicircular outline, commonly 5cm thick at the centre. Smooth, pale ochre-brown upper surface. The fine pores are creamy-white at first. Grows on the trunks and branches of living or dead birches. Once used as tinder, and also as a razor strop. Occurs all year round.

Lumpy Bracket
Trametes gibbosa

Size and description Fruit body 5–20cm. Thick annual cork-textured bracket fungus. Semicircular and slightly convex, and up to 15cm deep and 8cm thick. Upper surface greyish-white, irregular and lumpy, with a soft and velvety texture. Underside white or cream, then ochre, with radially elongated and creamy pores. Can be recognized with a fair degree of certainty by the fact that algae rapidly colonize the upper surface, turning it green.

Habitat Grows on the dead wood of deciduous trees, mainly beeches. Widespread and very common.

Season All year round.

Blushing Bracket

Daedaleopsis confragosa

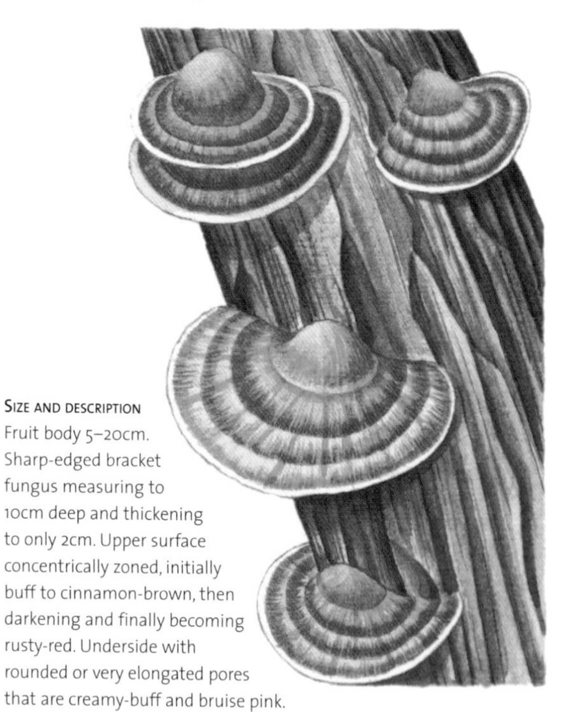

Size and description Fruit body 5–20cm. Sharp-edged bracket fungus measuring to 10cm deep and thickening to only 2cm. Upper surface concentrically zoned, initially buff to cinnamon-brown, then darkening and finally becoming rusty-red. Underside with rounded or very elongated pores that are creamy-buff and bruise pink.

Habitat May occur singly or in tiers on most dead deciduous trees, but most common on willows. Widespread and common.

Season All year round.

Hoof Fungus

Fomes fomentarius

Size and description Fruit body 10–25cm. Large and distinctive hoof-shaped bracket fungus. Surface colour variable, but usually shades of grey or pale brown, ridged and zoned with paler brown. Underside has rounded pores, initially cream, then light ochre or brown. A perennial fungus that is very hard and in the past was used as tinder. Fruit body can live for many years. Also called Tinder Bracket.

Habitat Common on birches in the north, particularly in the Scottish Highlands; occurs more rarely in southern England and Continental Europe.

Season All year round.

Many-zoned Polypore

Trametes versicolor

Size and description Fruit body 3–8cm. The most common bracket fungus. Semicircular or shell shaped with a thin undulating margin; may form a rosette when growing horizontally. Upper surface zoned in many colours, and overall may range from buff to black. It is silky when young, but this disappears with age. Underside pale buff, consisting of fine pores. Also called Turkeytail.

Habitat Grows in large overlapping groups on the wood of deciduous trees and shrubs. Widespread and very common.

Season All year round.

Beefsteak Fungus

Fistulina hepatica

Size and description
Fruit body 10–25cm. Bracket large and usually single, although several may grow above one another. Shaped like a liver or tongue, with the colour and texture of raw meat. Pinkish-red above, becoming orange-red and eventually dark brown. Spore-bearing surface underneath whitish, turning brown with age. Flesh whitish turning red and oozing blood-red juice, thick, soft and succulent. Also called Oak Tongue and Ox-tongue Fungus.

Habitat Grows on the lower trunks of deciduous trees, particularly oaks and Sweet Chestnuts, generating brown rot. Widespread and common across Europe.

Season Midsummer to autumn.

Dryad's Saddle

Polyporus squamosus

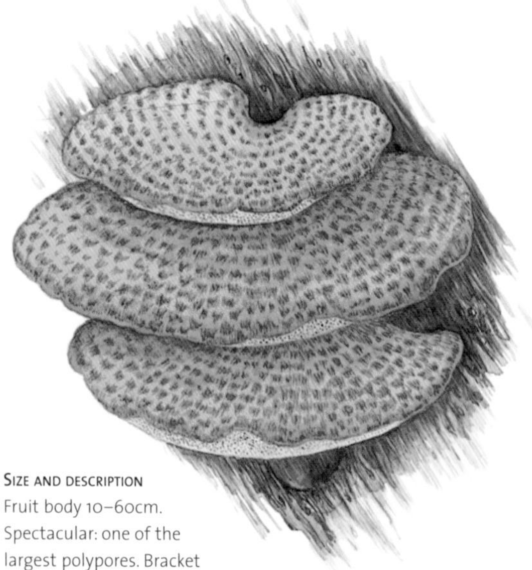

Size and description
Fruit body 10–60cm. Spectacular: one of the largest polypores. Bracket semicircular or fan shaped, anchored to wood by a short brown stem. Upper surface creamy-yellow to brown with concentric bands of triangular brown scales. Spore-bearing surface underneath cream or ochre. Flesh whitish, thick and leathery with a strong mealy odour.
Habitat Grows in clumps or clusters on deciduous trees, particularly beeches, elms and Sycamores, and dead or dying trees, logs and stumps, generating white rot. Common and widespread in Europe.
Season Midsummer to late autumn.

Wrinkled Crust

Phlebia radiata

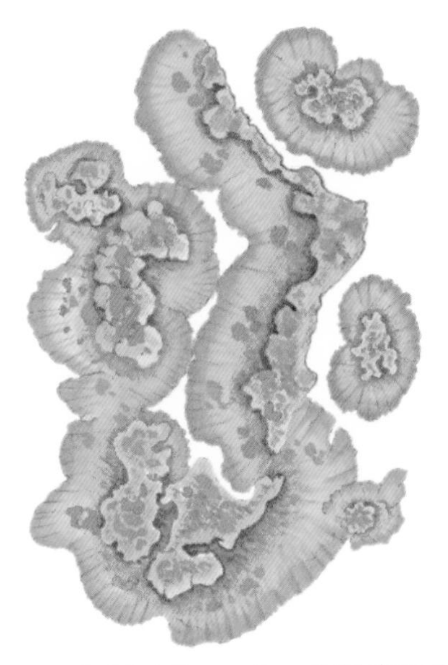

Size and description Fruit body 8–10cm. Grows in flat sheets. Growing edge bright orange-red fading to greyish in the centre. Surface develops wrinkles at right angles to the edge. If it encounters moss in its growth it will form around it, so destroying the radiating pattern. Dull-coloured specimens also occur.

Habitat Found on the surface of dead wood of deciduous trees. Widespread and common.

Season All year, but mainly autumn.

Jelly Rot

Phlebia tremellosa

Size and description Fruit body 1–5cm. Resupinate form is gelatinous and whitish; bracket form is thin and flexible with the lower surface ranging from orange and pinkish to buff. Upper surface of bracket form covered in white hairs. Grows flat at first, then bends outwards to form a shelf.

Habitat Grows on the surface of rotten deciduous wood. Widespread and common.

Season Mainly summer to autumn.

Hairy Curtain Crust

Stereum hirsutum

Size and description Fruit body 3–10cm. Tough and flexible bracket. Upper surface often zoned in shades of ochre and grey and covered in fine hairs. Underside varying shades of yellow. Below the bracket itself there may be a variable layer applied flat to the surface of the wood on which it lives. If the undersurface is bruised by rubbing hard it remains unchanged.

Habitat Grows in tiers on the dead wood of deciduous trees and shrubs. Widespread and very common.

Season All year round.

Southern Bracket

Ganoderma australe

Size and description Fruit body 10–60cm. Very large and impressive semicircular bracket fungus. Surface reddish-brown in colour, wrinkled and grooved in concentric zones; softer creamy margin during growth. Pores fine and pale, turning brown when scratched. A perennial, growing in layer upon layer below the original bracket. Because it is of a woody consistency its weight is considerable. In winter, cocoa-coloured spores form a brown dust around and on the fungus.

Habitat Grows singly, or in groups that are often tiered, on the living or dead wood of deciduous trees, particularly beeches. Widespread and common.

Season All year round.

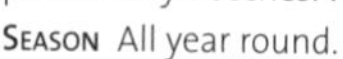

Brown Goblet

Coltricia perennis

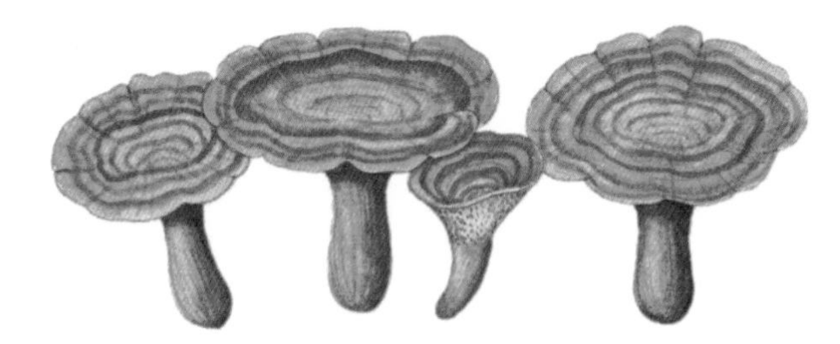

Size and description Cap to 8cm; stem to 3.5cm. A centrally stalked annual fungus. Upper surface first velvety, then smooth; concentrically zoned in many shades of brown. Underside has rounded or angular cinnamon-brown pores. Flesh brown, thin and corky, and harder when dry. Stem usually short. Adjacent fruit bodies may be fused so that it appears to have multiple stems. Sometimes used in floral decorations. Also called Tiger's Eye.

Habitat Grows on the ground, usually on sandy acid soils, often under pines. Widespread and common.

Season All year round.

Antler Fungus

Clavulinopsis corniculata

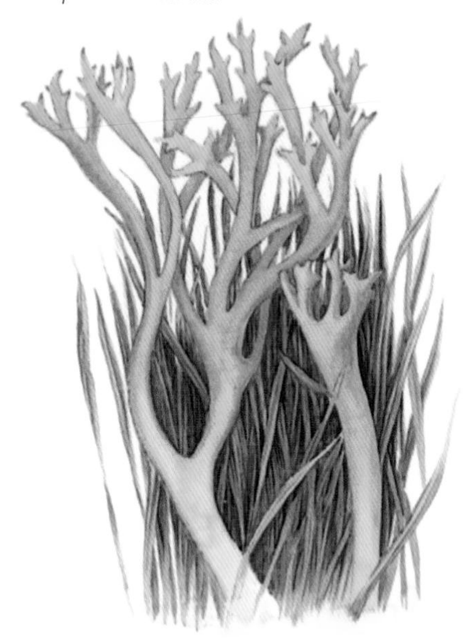

Size and description Height 2–8cm; variable diameter. Fruit body bright egg-yolk yellow with white colouration near the base; regularly branched with incurved crescentic tips giving an antler-like appearance. Flesh bright yellow and fragile with a mealy odour.
Habitat Grows on soil in short grass and open grassy woodland. Widespread but rare in Europe.
Season Midsummer to late autumn.

White Spindles
Clavaria fragilis

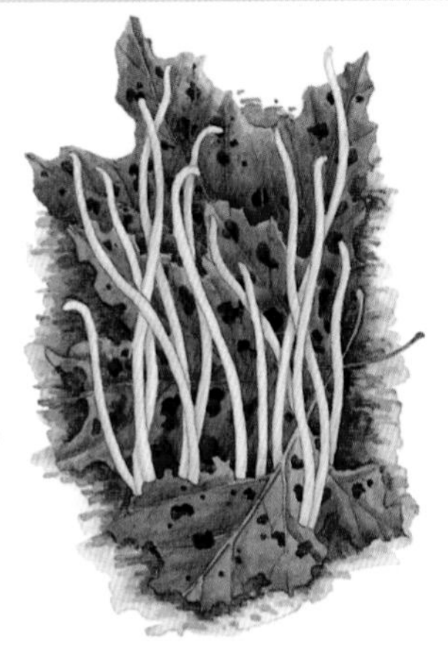

Height 3–12cm; diameter 0.3–0.7cm. Fruit body white tending to yellowish at the tip and base; smooth and laterally compressed with a longitudinal groove. Flesh white, brittle and watery with an earthy odour. Grows on soil singly or in clusters in or near woodland. Widely distributed and quite common across Europe. Occurs midsummer to autumn.

Yellow Club
Clavulinopsis helvola

Height 3–7cm; diameter 0.2–0.4cm. Consists of a group of pale yellow or orange-yellow 'stalks' with blunt tips. Grows in small groups in short grass, and among herbs in deciduous woodland. Widespread and common. Occurs midsummer to autumn.

Field Club

Clavaria argillacea

Size and description Height 3–8cm; diameter 0.2–0.8cm. Fruit body smooth, club shaped and pale greenish- or creamy-yellow, with the tapering stem tending to deeper yellow. Flesh pale yellow and brittle. Also called Moor Club.

Habitat Grows on soil in small clusters among moss on sandy heaths. Widespread across Europe.

Season Late summer.

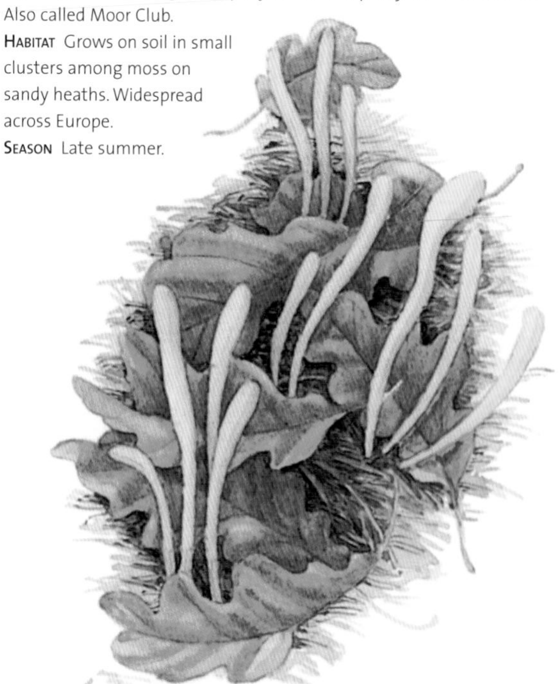

Giant Club

Clavariadelphus pistillaris

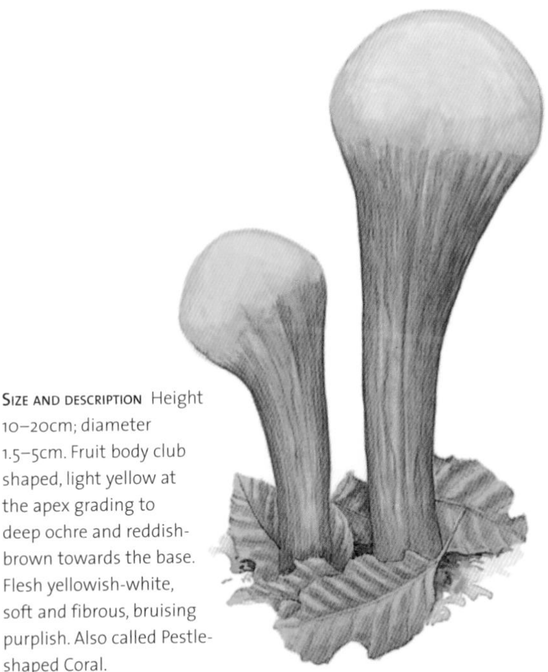

Size and description Height 10–20cm; diameter 1.5–5cm. Fruit body club shaped, light yellow at the apex grading to deep ochre and reddish-brown towards the base. Flesh yellowish-white, soft and fibrous, bruising purplish. Also called Pestle-shaped Coral.

Habitat Grows singly or in small groups on calcareous soil in beech woods or with pines at higher localities. Quite rare and patchily distributed in southern Britain and Europe.

Season Late summer to late autumn.

Wrinkled Coral Fungus

Clavulina rugosa

Height 5–12cm; variable diameter. Fruit body white, sometimes with a greyish tinge. Shaped either like a simple club, or has irregular branches with blunt tips. Surface irregular, wrinkled and twisted. Flesh white, soft and thick. Grows in soil in mixed woodland often adjacent to paths. Common and widespread across Europe. Occurs late summer to late autumn.

Grey Coral Fungus

Clavulina cinerea

Height 3–10cm; variable diameter. Fruit body ash-grey, repeatedly branched into dense antler-like clusters with blunt tips. Flesh greyish-white, soft but tough. Grows on soil in mixed woodland often adjacent to paths, forming solitary tufts or dense clusters. Widespread and common across Europe. Occurs midsummer to late autumn.

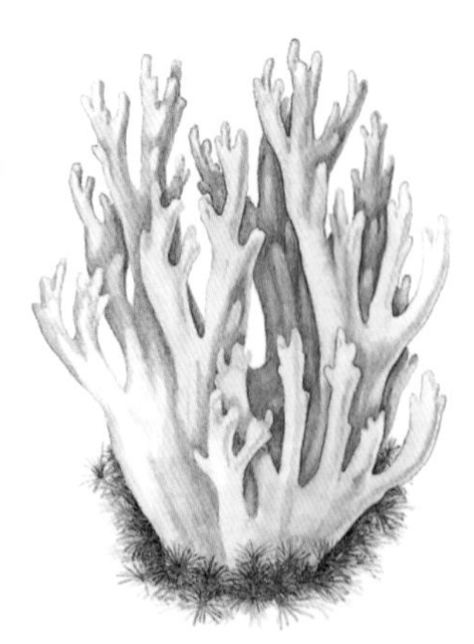

White Coral Fungus

Clavulina coralloides

Size and description Height 2–8cm; variable diameter. Fruit body whitish, densely tufted and repeatedly branched with crest-like fringes at the tips. Flesh white, soft and moderately tough. Also called Crested Coral Fungus.

Habitat Grows in soil in large numbers, in both deciduous and coniferous woodland. Common and widespread across Europe.

Season Early summer to late autumn.

Upright Coral

Ramaria stricta

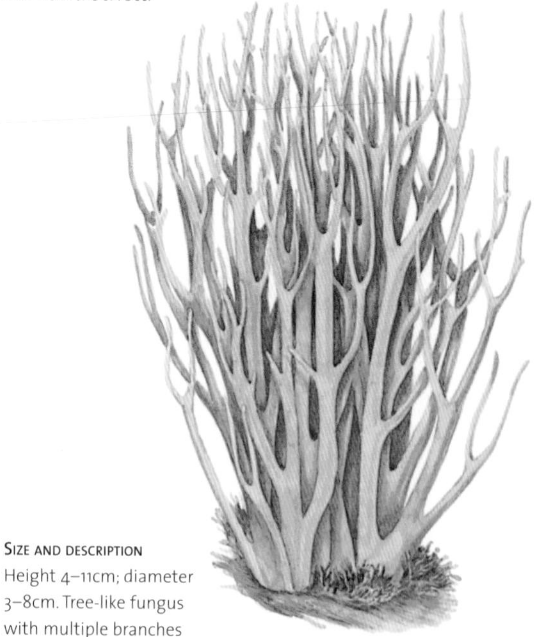

Size and description
Height 4–11cm; diameter 3–8cm. Tree-like fungus with multiple branches ascending vertically; pale cinnamon-brown to flesh coloured, paling at the tips. Flesh white discolouring to brown, with an earthy odour.

Habitat Grows on the fallen branches and stumps of deciduous and coniferous trees, particularly beeches. Common and widespread throughout Europe.

Season Midsummer to late autumn.

Clustered Coral

Ramaria botrytis

Size and description Height 7–15cm; diameter 5–20cm. White at first, becoming tan or ochre, then coral-pink as it branches repeatedly, finally forming wine-red forked and pointed tips, resembling a cauliflower with a thick basal stem. Flesh white, soft and firm with a fruity odour.

Habitat Grows in soil in deciduous woodland, particularly around beeches, favouring hilly districts. Unevenly distributed and rare in Europe.

Season Summer to early autumn.

Cauliflower Fungus

Sparassis crispa

Size and description Fruit body 10–60cm. Large fungus consisting of a much-branched and curled pale ochraceous-grey globe, in shape rather like a large curly lettuce, attached to tree by a short stem. Flesh is whitish. It is edible and pleasant when young and fresh, with a taste of anise, but it is difficult to remove all the sand that collects between its lobes. Also called Brain Fungus.

Habitat Grows in coniferous woodland, usually at the bases of pine trees. Widespread but rare in Europe.

Season Midsummer to late autumn.

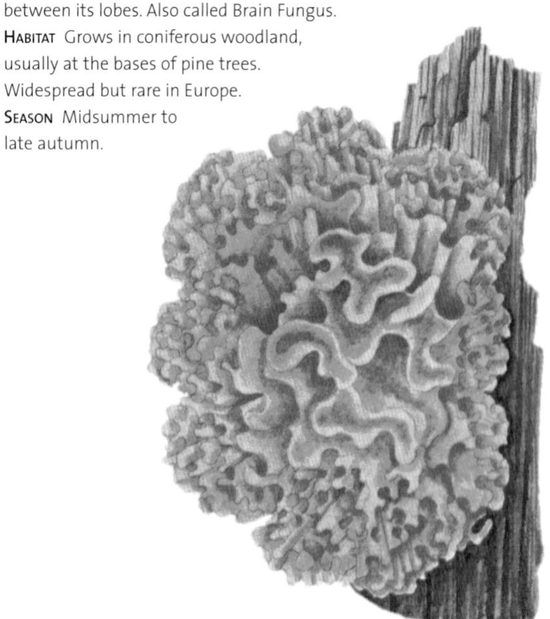

Common Stinkhorn

Phallus impudicus

Size and description Egg diameter 3–6cm; receptacle height 10–25cm. Starts as a soft whitish ball (the 'egg') full of a jelly-like mass. When mature the case splits, and in a few hours the fruit body rises out of the volva, usually to a height of about 15cm. It consists of a fragile white structure capped by an oval mass of olive-green mucus containing the spores, and has a characteristic sickly smell. This attracts flies, which rapidly remove the mucus and so distribute the spores. Fungus has a powerful foul odour at maturity.

Habitat Grows singly or in small scattered groups in woodland, parks and gardens in association with rotten and particularly buried wood. Widespread with an uneven distribution.

Season Mid-summer to early winter.

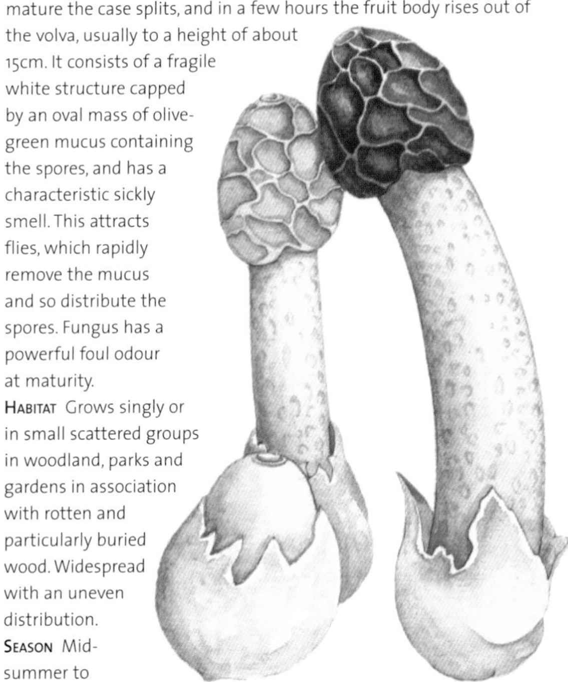

Dog Stinkhorn

Mutinus caninus

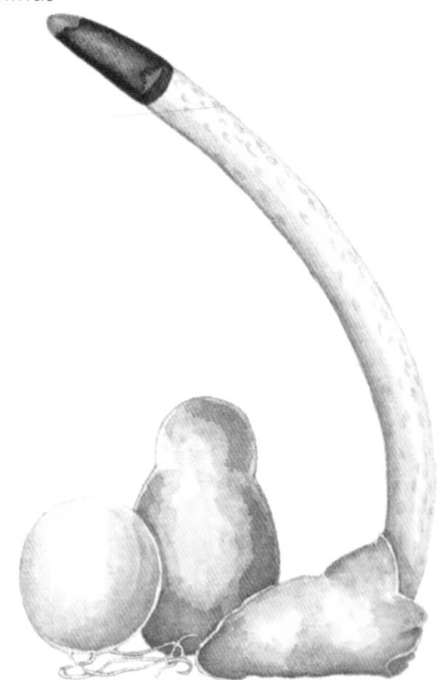

Size and description Egg diameter 1–2cm; receptacle height 10–12cm. Similar in growth to Common Stinkhorn (page 163). Egg whitish with a smooth surface that splits. Stem white, pitted, and once the gluten is removed the tip is quite a bright orange.

Habitat Grows in woodland leaf litter and around rotting wood. Infrequent but locally abundant.

Season Summer to late autumn.

Collared Earthstar

Geastrum triplex

Size and description Diameter to 10cm when fully opened. The most common of the earthstar fungi. Initially formed like a brown onion (bottom left). Outer layer then splits into 4–7 segments that fold back, leaving a central globe full of spores with an opening at its apex for their discharge (bottom right). Three-layered outer skin cracks as it folds back, often leaving an uncracked central disc like a cup in which the central globe sits (right).

Habitat Grows singly but more often in groups in the leaf litter of deciduous woodland and hedgerows. Widespread and locally common, particularly in southern and eastern England.

Season Late summer to autumn.

Grey Puffball

Bovista plumbea

Size and description Fruit body to 2.5cm. The size of a golfball or smaller. Smooth and initially creamy-white, but soon darkens to the colour of lead. Outer skin thin but tough, and once the spores have formed and dried the fungus is extremely light. It then becomes detached from the ground and blows along the surface in the wind, the spores being blown out of an apical opening. Flesh firm and white when young, later olive-green to brown and powdery.

Habitat Occurs in scattered groups on short grass in pastures and on lawns. Common and widely distributed in northern Europe.

Season Late summer to autumn.

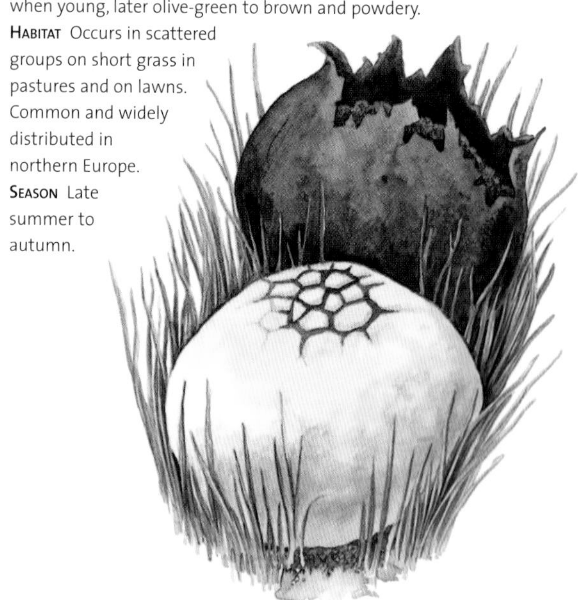

Brown Puffball

Bovista nigrescens

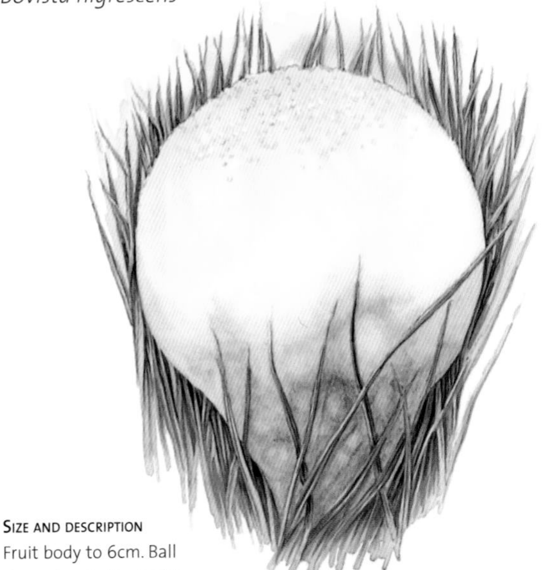

Size and description
Fruit body to 6cm. Ball shaped and attached to substrate by a single mycelial cord. White at first with the outer layer flaking away to expose a shiny blackish layer; apex then breaks open to release the powdery spores. Ripe fruit body often breaks away from the ground and rolls around in the wind. Flesh white and firm when young, then purplish-black and powdery.

Habitat Occurs in small groups on open grassland. Common and widely distributed; most common in north.

Season Midsummer to late autumn.

Giant Puffball

Calvatia gigantea

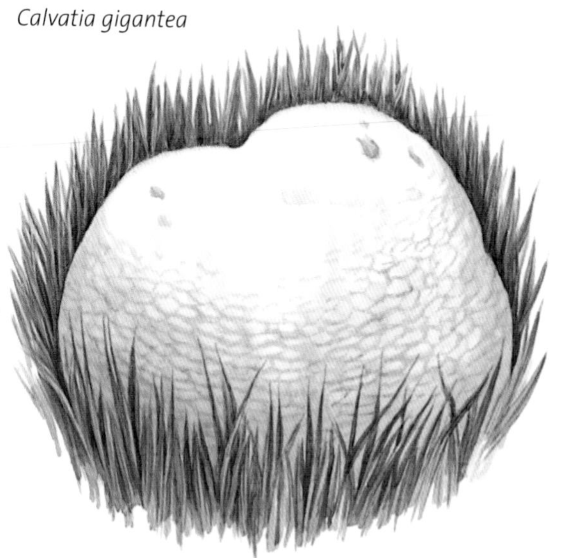

Size and description Fruit body to 70cm. Ball shaped and attached to the ground by several mycelial cords. White and leathery, becoming brownish-yellow when old and finally splitting to release the spore mass. Mycelial cords eventually break and the fruit body rolls around in the wind, aiding spore dispersal. Flesh firm and white when young, later rusty-brown and powdery.

Habitat Occurs singly or in small troops in fields and woodland, under hedges and on waste ground on rich soil. Widespread although uncommon in Europe.

Season Midsummer to autumn.

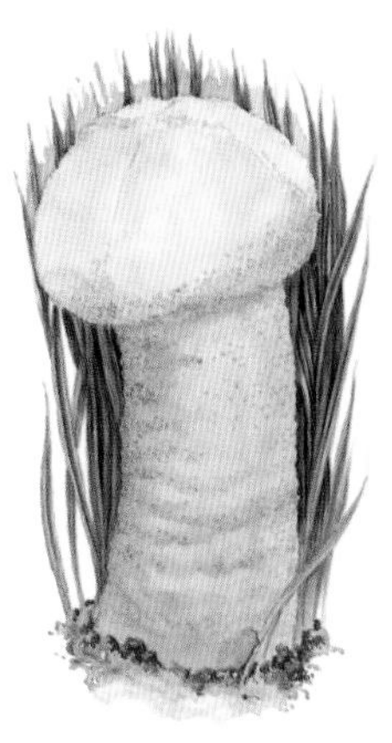

Stalked Puffball

Calvatia excipuliformis

Fruit body to 10cm; height to 20cm. Fruit body initially pale buff, later dull brown. Covered in small spines or warts that fall away to reveal the fragile inner wall, which eventually splits at the apex to release the spores. Empty bases then remain in place for many months. Flesh firm and white when young, later olive-brown and powdery. Grows in small groups on soil in pastures and deciduous woodland, and on heaths and waste ground. Common and widespread. Occurs late summer to autumn.

Mosaic Puffball

Lycoperdon utriforme

Fruit body to 15cm. Pear shaped when mature, tapering to form a stout wrinkled base. Whitish turning dark brown, with the outer surface cracking into hexagonal patches that fall away, leaving the fragile inner wall; eventually this splits to release the spores. Grows in groups on sandy soil in open grassland and woodland edges. Uncommon. Occurs early summer to autumn.

Common Puffball

Lycoperdon perlatum

Fruit body to 6cm. Club shaped with a tall cylindrical base. Initially pure white, later yellowish-brown. Surface with short pyramidal spines, each surrounded by a ring of smaller spines or warts. Spines soon loosen and rub off, leaving a characteristic pattern. Central spore mass at first white, then grey-black. Grows in groups, often in large numbers, among the leaf litter in mixed woodland. Widespread with an uneven distribution. Occurs early summer to winter.

Stump Puffball

Lycoperdon pyriforme

Fruit body to 4cm. Club shaped and attached to wood substrate by white mycelial cords. Yellowish-white and covered with small spines that soon fall off, leaving it smooth. Dark spores are discharged through a small central opening. Flesh initially firm and white, then olive-brown and powdery. Grows in large numbers on the stumps, logs and rotten wood of deciduous trees. Common and widespread. Occurs summer to early winter.

Meadow Puffball

Lycoperdon pratense

Size and description Fruit body to 4cm. Pear shaped and white, with small granules and scales that fall off, leaving it smooth. Upper fertile section is separated from the sterile stalk by a conspicuous membrane. Eventually the upper layer breaks off, leaving a brown bowl and stem. Flesh firm and white when young, becoming olive-brown and powdery once mature.

Habitat Occurs in groups in short grass, sometimes in large numbers. Widespread in Europe, with an uneven distribution.

Season Summer to early winter.

Common Earthball

Scleroderma citrinum

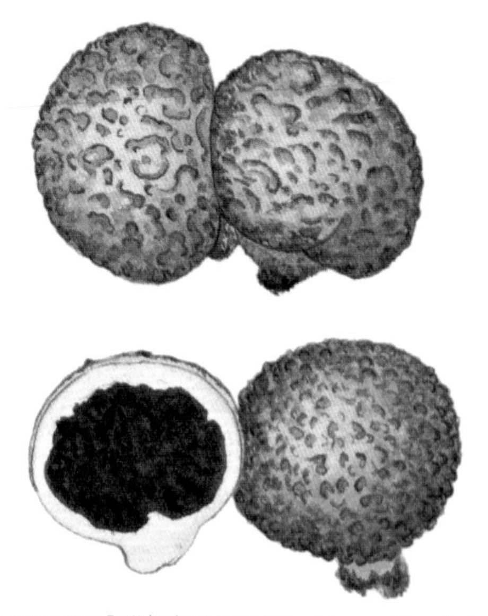

Size and description Fruit body to 10cm. Resembles an old cracked tennis ball. Roughly globose and with a thick skin, dark ochre-brown on the outside, which splits as it expands, showing more and more of the yellow inner layer. Centre comprises a black spore mass. The fungus has no opening for spore discharge, but splits irregularly.
Habitat Grows in woodland, favouring acid soils with deciduous trees such as oaks and birches. Widespread and common.
Season Late summer to early winter.

Yellow Stagshorn

Calocera viscosa

Size and description Height to 10cm. Branched antler-like fungus greatly varying in size, from a small growth only 2cm high, to a tree-like structure 10cm or sometimes more in height and branched several times. Colour bright egg-yolk yellow to orange. Flesh tough and gelatinous. Also called Stag's Horn Fungus.
Habitat Grows in tufts on the stumps and roots of coniferous trees, most frequently those of pines. May be attached to roots by long stems that penetrate deeply into the ground, thus appearing to be growing on soil. Widespread and very common.
Season Autumn.

Jew's Ear

Auricularia auricula-judae

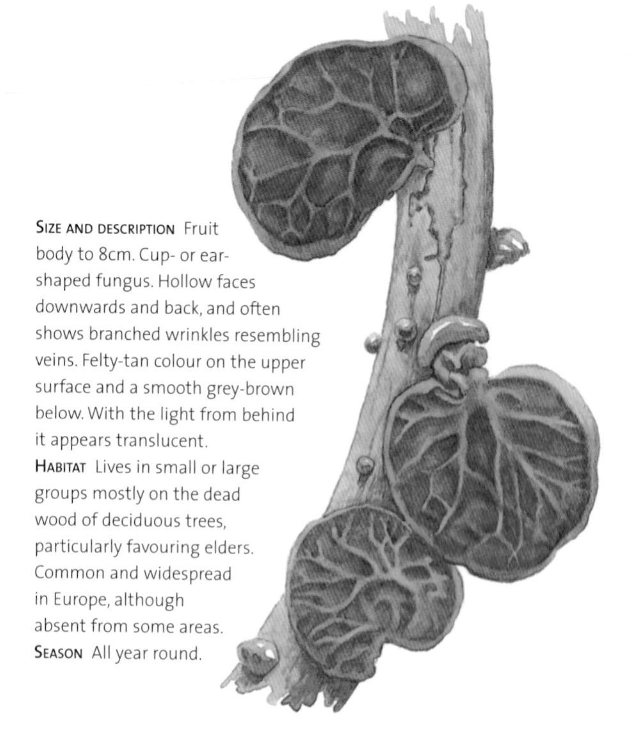

Size and description Fruit body to 8cm. Cup- or ear-shaped fungus. Hollow faces downwards and back, and often shows branched wrinkles resembling veins. Felty-tan colour on the upper surface and a smooth grey-brown below. With the light from behind it appears translucent.

Habitat Lives in small or large groups mostly on the dead wood of deciduous trees, particularly favouring elders. Common and widespread in Europe, although absent from some areas.

Season All year round.

Earthfan

Thelephora terrestris

Size and description Fruit body to 6cm. Consists of many small fan-shaped fruit bodies. Base colour reddish-brown, but darkens considerably with age. Surface covered in radiating fibres that overhang the edge as a white margin. Flesh brown, tough and fibrous. Because it has no means of supporting itself, it climbs up grasses, heather and in fact anything available.

Habitat Grows in clusters in association with the roots of conifers, favouring sandy soils. Widespread and common.

Season Summer to late autumn.

Scaly Hedgehog

Sarcodon imbricatus

Size and description Cap to 25cm. Yellowish-brown cap flattish at first, then concave bearing coarse dark brown scales. Spore-bearing layer underneath spiny and white when young, turning grey to purplish-brown with maturity. Flesh white and firm with a spicy odour. Stem thick and white.

Habitat Grows singly or in scattered groups on sandy soils in montane coniferous woodland, favouring pines and spruces. Occurs in northern Europe, including Scotland, but is rare.

Season July to November.

Wood Hedgehog

Hydnum repandum

Size and description Cap to 15cm. Cap pale buff or cream. No gills, but below the cap there are many spines 4–8mm long, slightly more pinkish than the cap; these are longest halfway in from the edge and run down the stem, becoming shorter. Spines are brittle and rub off. Flesh white, soft, thick and quite crumbly. Also called Urchin of the Woods and Pied de Mouton.

Habitat Grows singly and in groups in deciduous and coniferous woodland. Widespread but infrequent.

Season Late summer to late autumn.

Purple Jellydisc

Ascocoryne sarcoides

Size and description Disc to 1.5cm. Jelly-like fungus with a short stem. Consists of reddish-purple 'jelly-blobs' clustered together and recognizable by their colour. Not all become mature, but when they do they become top shaped with a flat upper surface. Flesh is pinkish-purple and gelatinous. Also called Jelly Drops.

Habitat Grows in clusters, mainly on the dead trunks and branches of deciduous fallen trees. Common and widespread.

Season Late summer to early winter.

Green Wood Cup

Chlorociboria aeruginascens

Size and description Disc to 0.5cm. Tiny bright fungus. Fruit body bright verdigris green, and flattened or cup shaped; upper surface smooth, lower surface finely downy, tapering to a very short and slim stem. Flesh concolorous and thin. Mycelium stains wood green and is more often seen than the fruit bodies. The coloured wood was formerly used in the decorated boxes known as Tunbridgeware. Also called Green Elf Cup.

Habitat Grows in small clusters, often densely massed, on the rotting wood of deciduous trees, particularly oaks. Common and widespread.

Season Late summer to winter.

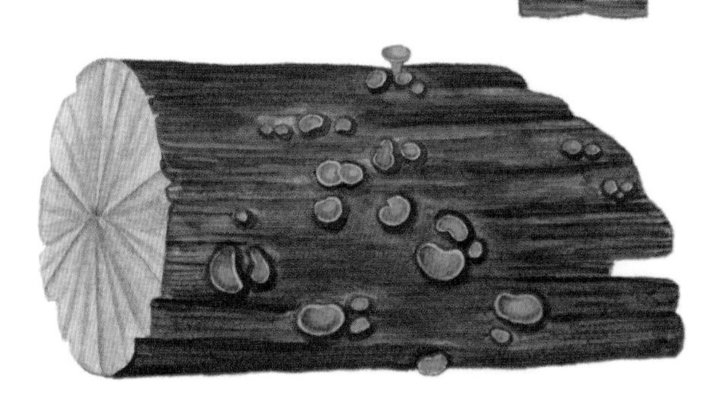

White Saddle

Helvella crispa

Size and description Cap to 6cm; stem to 12cm. Distinctive shape of fungus makes it easy to recognize. Cap very pale grey to whitish, curly and may vary greatly in shape, but always sits on a deeply furrowed white stem. Flesh white and brittle. Also called White Helvella.

Habitat Occurs singly or in small groups in the grass or leaf litter of deciduous woods. Common and widespread in Europe.

Season Midsummer to late autumn.

Elfin Saddle

Helvella lacunosa

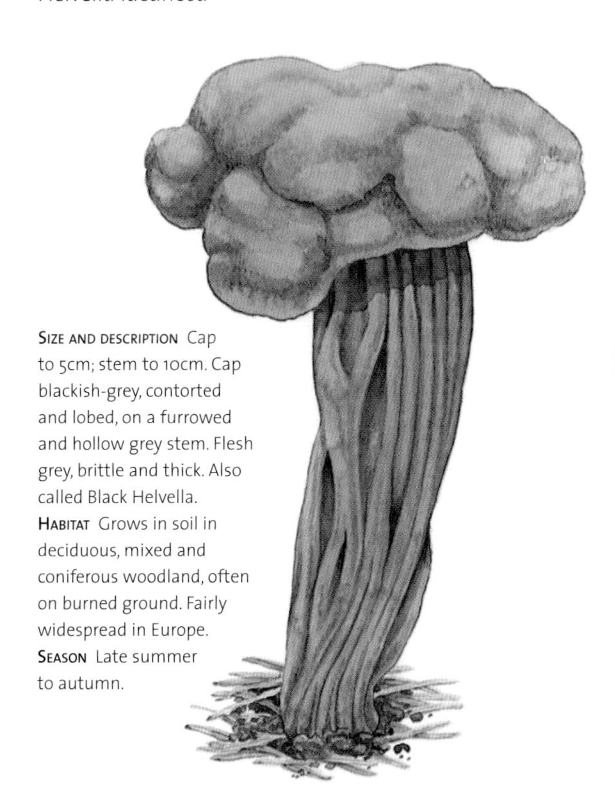

Size and description Cap to 5cm; stem to 10cm. Cap blackish-grey, contorted and lobed, on a furrowed and hollow grey stem. Flesh grey, brittle and thick. Also called Black Helvella.

Habitat Grows in soil in deciduous, mixed and coniferous woodland, often on burned ground. Fairly widespread in Europe.

Season Late summer to autumn.

Orange Peel Fungus

Aleuria aurantia

Size and description Cup to 10cm. Brightest of the most common cup fungi. Forms cups or irregular discs of various sizes, to 4cm tall. Inner surface bright orange, outer surface orange-grey; resembles orange peel turned inside-out. Initially cup shaped, becoming more saucer-like and irregular with maturity. Flesh pallid, thin and brittle.

Habitat Grows in woodland, on embankments and in short grass or herbage on bare soil. Common and widespread in Europe.

Season Late summer to late autumn.

Pig's Ears

Peziza badia

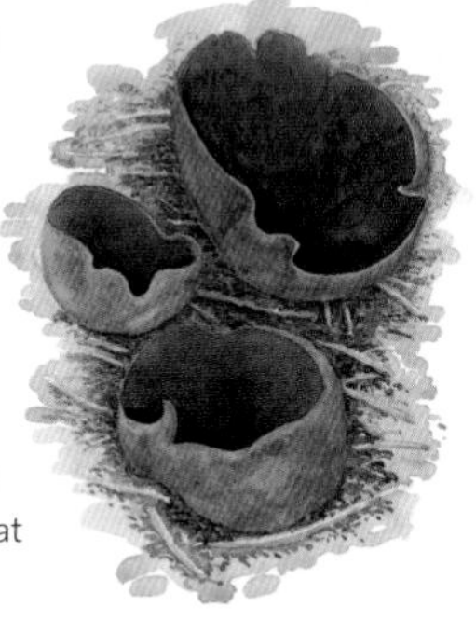

Cup to 8cm. Small, irregular and brown with a wavy margin and no stem. Upper surface dark olive-brown, particularly near the centre. Lower surface more pallid reddish-brown. Flesh reddish-brown, brittle and thin. Grows in small troops, some fused, on soil in woodland, particularly favouring clay banks and bare paths. Common in temperate lowlands across Europe. One of many similar species that are difficult to identify in the field. Occurs late summer to late autumn.

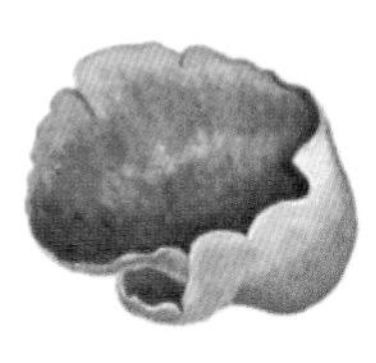

Palamino Cup

Peziza repanda

Size and description Cup to 12cm. Cup-shaped fungus. Inner surface pale brownish-buff, exterior slightly paler. Edge becomes wavy in larger specimens and is usually toothed. Grows singly or in small troops on soil around stumps, and rotting sawdust and wood. Occurs late spring to late autumn. Uncommon.

Scarlet Elf Cup

Sarcoscypha austriaca

Size and description Cup to 5cm. Red, reddish or pink fungus up to 1.5cm tall. Inner surface bright scarlet, outer surface paler and covered in matted white hairs. Margin becomes tattered as it expands. Cup-shaped fruit body has a narrow short stem. Flesh pale and brittle.
Habitat Gregarious, growing on dead wood. Quite common in continental Europe, and in Britain found particularly in the east. *S. coccinea*, a very similar species, is more frequent in the west. The two species can only be distinguished from each other by microscopic features.
Season Early winter to early spring.

Common Morel

Morchella esculenta

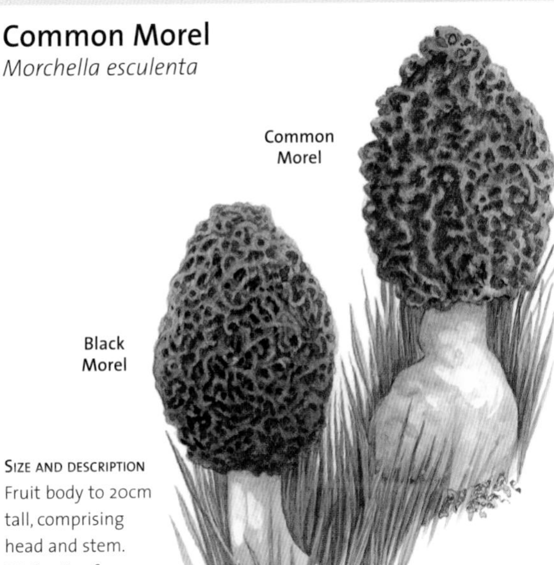

Size and description Fruit body to 20cm tall, comprising head and stem. Distinctive fungus highly regarded as a table delicacy. Cap variably brown, wrinkled and oval or conical. Stem white and thick. Flesh white, brittle and thin.

Habitat Grows singly or in scattered troops on calcareous soil and burned ground in damp deciduous woodland. Often found among ash trees. Widespread but uncommon over much of Europe.

Season Spring.

Similar species **Black Morel** *(M. elata)*. Fruit body to 15cm tall. Cap pointed and conical with pits in vertical rows. Of more northerly distribution, smaller and generally even rarer than Common Morel.

Beech Woodwart

Hypoxylon fragiforme

Size and description Fruit body to 1cm. Tiny fungus. Appears as small spheres (the fruit body, or stroma) that are rusty-red at first, then become black. Surface minutely rough. Red phase is short-lived and tends to occur in late summer, so the fungus is usually encountered later in the season in the black state, in which it is very persistent.
Habitat Grows in masses on the trunks and branches of dead beeches that still have bark attached. Widespread and very common.
Season All year round.

King Alfred's Cakes

Daldinia concentrica

SIZE AND DESCRIPTION Fruit body to 10cm. Forms in successive layers, appearing as round and shiny black lumps. Initially covered with a reddish spore layer, but this washes off, leaving the black surface. If cut in half the fungus can be seen to be composed of concentric layers of very dark to very light grey material. Also called Cramp Balls because it is said to relieve cramps.

HABITAT Grows on ash trees, and rarely on other deciduous trees. Different species can be found on other hosts.

SEASON All year round; old specimens persist for many years.

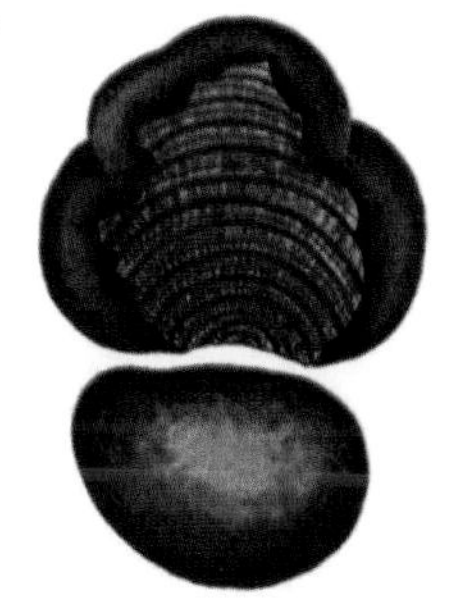

Candlesnuff Fungus

Xylaria hypoxylon

Size and description Height 3–5cm. One of the most common fungi on dead wood of all kinds. Consists of flattened black stems that arise vertically from wood and usually (but not always) branch into 2–5-pointed antler-like extensions. These are white at first, then blacken as they mature until eventually the whole fungus is black.

Habitat Grows singly or in groups on dead wood, particularly the rotting stumps of deciduous trees, favouring ash trees. Widespread and common.

Season All year round.

Summer Truffle

Tuber aestivum

Size and description Fruit body to 7cm. A rare and prized edible species. Fruit body irregularly spherical with a blackish-brown surface covered in pyramidal warts. Solid interior yellowish-grey to brown marbled with whitish veins.

Habitat Grows underground in calcareous soils at about 2–10cm in depth, typically in association with beeches, and less often with Sweet Chestnuts and evergreen oaks. In Britain found only in southern England, where it is rare; more common in central and southern Europe.

Season Summer to autumn.

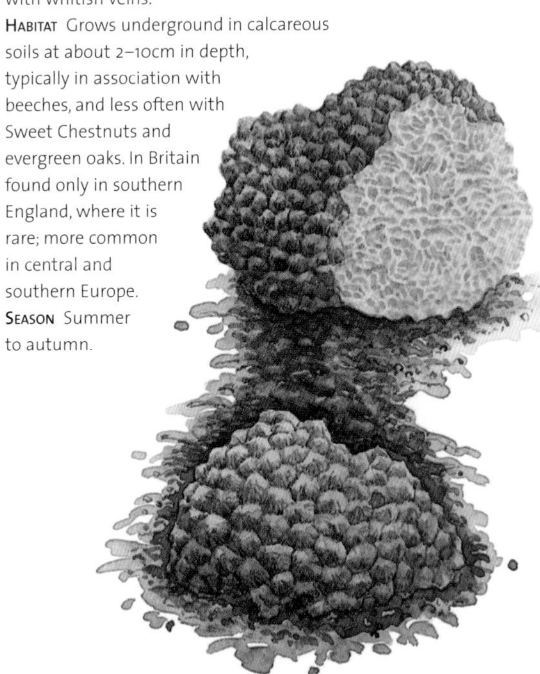

names